Nutrition

Eating for
Good Health

United States
Department of
Agriculture

Agriculture Information
Bulletin 685

Foreword

by Mike Espy
Secretary of Agriculture

The essence of the agricultural enterprise is providing food, the right food to sustain people's life and their health. As Secretary of Agriculture, I am deeply concerned that all Americans have enough food to eat, but I also want people to have enough information to know what to eat.

I believe that safeguarding the nutritional content of food is as essential as maintaining its abundant supply. Access to food itself—and also to information about a healthy diet and the safe handling of food—is a right of all Americans. A healthy diet is the cornerstone of good health.

Nutrition: Eating for Good Health presents all aspects of nutrition for which the U.S. Department of Agriculture has responsibility, including nutrition guidance, Federal food assistance programs, and state-of-the-art research findings on what nutrients are needed by different groups in our society and how these nutrients affect our health and well-being.

More than half of the U.S. Department of Agriculture's $68 billion budget is spent on nutrition programs. Some of these programs feed more than 25 million children lunch each school day or provide groceries for more than 27 million families through the Food Stamp program.

This book was written and produced for those who are interested in eating for good health, and that includes most of us. It will be of special interest to people who work in the field of nutrition and meal planning, agricultural producers, educators, and students.

The content of *Nutrition: Eating for Good Health* was written as part of the annual Yearbook of Agriculture project.

As an institution, the agriculture yearbooks of the past century have served their original purpose. Yearbooks have disseminated information about agriculture (in the most comprehensive sense of the word) to the people of the United States, with a special focus on farmers. Now, a single volume is no longer adequate to meet the original mission of the Yearbook of Agriculture. Nor is it a cost-effective means of disseminating information in our fast-changing, multimedia world. We agreed with the U.S. Congress that the time had come to retire the Yearbook of Agriculture series.

Since the research and writing had already been completed for this manuscript early this year, we decided to provide the information to American consumers as a single volume on nutrition. USDA will continue to provide information on key topics of interest to the American people as a whole, and to the special people we serve, including farmers and consumers, environmentalists and school children. We will use new technologies to deliver information that people need, where and when they need it, and in a form they can use.

I hope you find the information provided in *Nutrition: Eating for Good Health* useful. At the back of the book you will find a section on how to get more information on nutrition issues. Let us hear from you.

Contents

Contents

PART III. Domestic Food Assistance Programs

Contents

Your
Food
Choices

PART 1

Diets of Americans

Cecilia Wilkinson Enns
Katherine S. Tippett
Peter Basiotis
and
Joseph Goldman
Human Nutrition
Information Service, USDA,
Hyattsville, MD

American eating habits more closely follow national dietary guidelines than they did a decade ago, but there's plenty of room for improvement.

There was a shift to a lower-fat, higher-carbohydrate diet between 1977-78 and 1989-90, according to surveys conducted by USDA's Human Nutrition Information Service. But the amount of fat in the average diet is still higher than recommended. And Americans are still not eating the amounts of fruits, vegetables, grains and low-fat dairy products that are recommended in the latest dietary guidance, the Food Guide Pyramid (see next page). For example, almost a quarter of the population ate no fruit in the 3 days of the 1989-90 survey period.

The most recent survey participants were asked to provide dietary data for three consecutive days, first in a personal interview and then by filling out forms. Estimates discussed here are averages for the 7,780 individuals who participated and are compared with data collected in a 1977-78 survey.

The results show a Nation that's eating more in conformance with the Food Guide Pyramid, which places bread, cereal, rice, and pasta at the base and fats, oils, and sweets at the tip, but we still have much to learn. The food intake results are grouped below as they're grouped in the Food Guide Pyramid.

Bread, Cereal, Rice, and Pasta Group

Americans are certainly eating more grains. The average intake of grain products increased from 213 grams in 1977-78 to 254 grams in 1989-90—a 19-percent increase (table 1).

Almost everyone ate at least one grain product over the survey period. There were practically no differences in total grain products eaten at different income levels. (Total grains include breads, cereals, pastas, cakes, cookies, pies, grain mixtures, etc.) Teenage boys ate the most total grain products, while women over 30 and young children ate the least. Men and women 20 to 29 and 40 to 49 years of age were the least likely to eat cereals and pastas, and generally ate the smallest amounts.

In 1989-90, males 6 to 39 and females 6 to 29 ate the largest amounts of grain mixtures—mixtures with a grain product as the main ingredient, such as pizza, tacos, or macaroni and cheese. Although the older age groups ate smaller amounts of grain mixtures than the younger groups, all groups ate more in 1989-90 than people the same age did a decade earlier.

Fruit Group

Americans ate about the same amount of fruit in 1989-90 as in 1977-78, but some people are eating little or no fruit. More than a fourth of the population ate no fruit and drank no fruit juice during the 3 consecutive days of record-keeping.

A larger proportion of low-income people (33 percent) ate no fruit than did high-income people (23 percent). Men 20 years old and over were more likely than women 20 and over to eat no fruit. In the low- income population, no fruit was eaten in 3 days by 39 percent of teenage boys and by 43 percent of men 20 years and older (fig. 1). More than half (52 percent) of the people who reported that they did not have enough to eat did not eat fruit over the 3 survey days.

Only 2 percent of high-income elderly women and 4 percent of middle-income elderly women ate or drank no fruit or fruit juices in the 3 days, compared with 19 percent of low-income elderly women. A higher proportion of low-income blacks (36 percent) than high-income blacks (25 percent) consumed no fruit or fruit juice.

Food Guide Pyramid
A Guide to Daily Food Choices

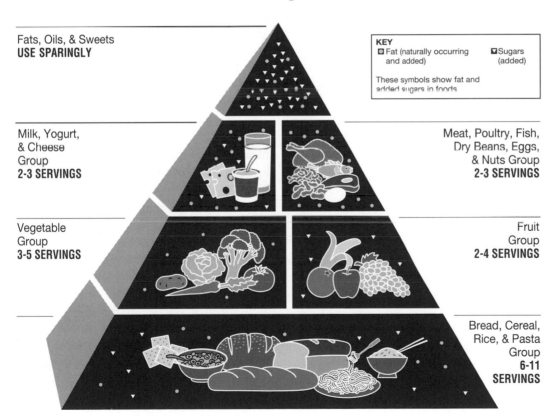

Fats, Oils, & Sweets
USE SPARINGLY

KEY
☐ Fat (naturally occurring and added)   ☑ Sugars (added)

These symbols show fat and added sugars in foods

Milk, Yogurt, & Cheese Group
2-3 SERVINGS

Meat, Poultry, Fish, Dry Beans, Eggs, & Nuts Group
2-3 SERVINGS

Vegetable Group
3-5 SERVINGS

Fruit Group
2-4 SERVINGS

Bread, Cereal, Rice, & Pasta Group
6-11 SERVINGS

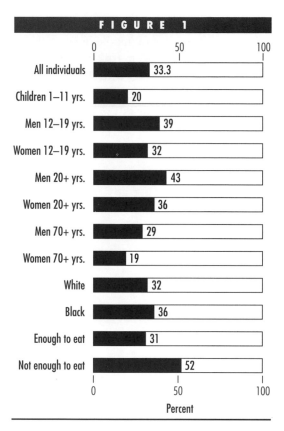

Percentage of the low-income population consuming no fruit, 3 days, 1989-90

FIGURE 1

	Percent
All individuals	33.3
Children 1–11 yrs.	20
Men 12–19 yrs.	39
Women 12–19 yrs.	32
Men 20+ yrs.	43
Women 20+ yrs.	36
Men 70+ yrs.	29
Women 70+ yrs.	19
White	32
Black	36
Enough to eat	31
Not enough to eat	52

Vegetable Group

The average daily intake of vegetables was slightly lower in 1989-90 than in 1977-78—179 grams versus 198 grams (a cup of lettuce weighs 55 grams and one medium raw tomato, 123 grams). These numbers do not include vegetables eaten as parts of mixtures, which frequently include vegetables.

Most individuals ate at least one vegetable over the 3-day survey period. Vegetable intakes in 1989-90 were lower for the low-income group (145 grams) than for the high-income group (197 grams).

For both sexes, total vegetable intake generally increased with age. A greater proportion of the vegetables eaten by younger than older people was white potatoes, including french fries and potato chips. For example, white potatoes accounted for 49 percent of the vegetables eaten by males age 12 to 19, but for only 25 percent of the vegetables eaten by males age 60 to 69. Overall, about 15 percent of the intake of white potatoes was french fries. The proportion of white potatoes eaten as french fries was highest among males under 30 and females under 20 years of age.

In dietary recommendations, legumes (dry beans and peas) are counted either as meat alternates or as vegetables. Only about 25 percent of individuals ate legumes over the 3-day period of the surveys.

Meat, Poultry, Fish, Beans, Eggs, and Nuts Group

Total intake of meat, poultry, and fish dropped slightly, from 204 grams in 1977-78 to 184 grams in 1989-90—a 10-percent decrease. In 1989-90, the amount of meat, poultry, and fish consumed was higher in the high-income group (198 grams) than in the low-income group (160 grams).

In 1977-78, red meats (beef, pork, lamb, veal, and organ meats) accounted for the largest share of the total consumption of meat, poultry, and fish; in 1989-90, mixtures made up the largest share. There was little change between the two survey periods in the con-

TABLE 1

Food intakes: Average intake* per individual per day and percent of individuals using at least once in 3 days, 1977-78 and 1989-90

Food group	Average intake		Percent using	
	1977-78	1989-90	1977-78	1989-90
Meat, poultry, fish	204	184	99	98
Mixtures	69	83	60	65
Beef	50	27	68	49
Pork	20	12	50	38
Milk and milk products	322	292	94	94
Whole milk	128	87	47	37
Lowfat and skim milk	66	137	24	48
Eggs	26	17	55	41
Grain products	213	254	99	99
Mixtures	52	84	45	60
Cereals and pastas	50	67	67	72
Vegetables	198	179	98	96
Potatoes	62	59	79	75
Fruits	142	150	73	74
Citrus	64	62	46	43
Noncitrus	76	85	58	60
Juices and nectars	12	22	10	15
Soft drinks	141	238	52	63
Low-calorie	20	62	8	20

* Average per individual, whether or not the individual used food from the group. Average intakes per user would be higher.

sumption of poultry; fish and shellfish; and frankfurters, sausages, and luncheon meats.

Many foods are mixtures of two or more ingredients. For example, a sandwich is a mixture of bread and fillings. Mixtures reported as a single item (for example, a ham sandwich) are usually included as a single item in the food group of the major ingredient (in this case, ham). "Mixtures mainly meat, poultry, or fish" (meat mixtures) are defined as mixtures having meat, poultry, or fish as a main ingredient, such as beef potpie, chicken cacciatore, or tuna-noodle casserole.

In 1989-90, Americans ate more meat mixtures than in 1977-78; the amount of meat mixtures was up by about one-fifth—from 69 grams to 83 grams. The proportion of individuals who ate meat mixtures at least once in 3 days increased from 60 to 65 percent.

A lot of those mixtures come as hamburgers. About 17 percent of the survey respondents ate a hamburger (or cheeseburger or pizzaburger) on a bun at least once in 3 days in 1989-90; more boys and men 12 to 29 and girls 6 to 19 years old ate hamburgers than did people in other age groups. The percentage of individuals eating hamburgers was twice as high among blacks as among whites, was higher in the South than in other regions, and was higher in the middle- than in the low- or high-income groups.

About 41 percent of individuals ate eggs at least once in 3 days in 1989-90, down from 55 percent in 1977-78. In 1989-90, the proportions of individuals who reported eating eggs were highest among children 1 to 2 years old, men

20 to 39 years old, men 60 and over, blacks, and low-income people.

Milk, Yogurt, and Cheese Group

In 1989-90, Americans drank about the same amount of total milk and milk products as they did in 1977-78. As a share of total milk and milk products, however, lowfat and skim milk went up while whole milk went down between the two surveys. Milk desserts and cheese stayed the same. "Other fluid milk," which includes milk not specified as to type, was a much larger share of the total in 1977-78 than in 1989-90; more people specified the fat content of their milk in the most recent survey, perhaps reflecting increased awareness of fat in the diet.

In 1989-90, children and teenagers drank the most fluid milk and men and women age 40 to 69 drank the least (figure 2). Overall, 60 percent of the milk we drank was lowfat or skim, and older age groups generally drank larger proportions of their milk as lowfat or skim milk. The proportion of fluid milk intake that was lowfat or skim milk was much lower among blacks (23 percent) than among whites (65 percent). Low-income people (those with household incomes below 131 percent of the Federal poverty level) drank 37 percent of their milk as lowfat or skim, compared with 58 percent for middle-income people (those with incomes 131 percent to 300 percent of poverty) and 72 percent for high-income people (those with income over 300 percent of poverty).

In 1977-78, people drank nearly twice as

much of both milk and coffee as they did of soft drinks; by 1989-90, the amounts of milk, coffee, and soft drinks were almost equal (table 2). While average milk and coffee consumption stayed about the same, soft drink consumption increased from 141 to 238 grams—an increase of 69 percent. Intake of low-calorie soft drinks more than tripled, from 20 grams in 1977-78 to 62 grams in 1989-90. A cup of milk weighs 245 grams; of black coffee, 240 grams; of soft drink, 248 grams. In 1989-90, men and women age 40 to 69 drank the most coffee. On the other hand, soft drinks were most popular with 12- to 49-year-olds. Overall, a little more than one-fourth of the soft drinks we drink are low-calorie. For women 50 to 69 years old, low-calorie soft drinks accounted for over half of total soft drink consumption. Low-income people and blacks drank less coffee, but more fruit drinks and ades than did people in the middle- and high-income groups and whites.

While some Americans are drinking lower-fat milk, many of them are drinking no milk at all—at least they did not during the 3 days covered by the survey. About a quarter of low-income and middle-income teenage girls did not drink milk in the 3 days. Only 3 percent in the highest income group drank no milk.

And elderly women at low and middle incomes were much less likely to drink milk than elderly women at the high-income level. Practically all children in the survey reported drinking milk.

Calcium is a current public health issue.

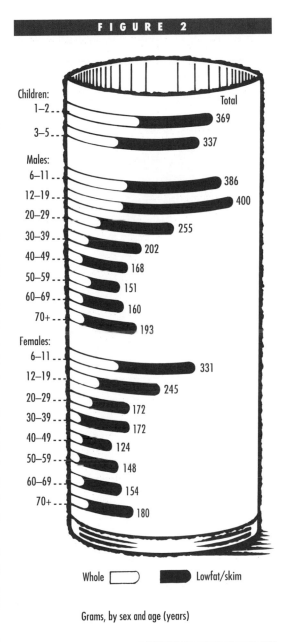

FIGURE 2

Milk intakes: Mean per day per individual, 3 days, 1989-90

Total

Children:
1–2 .. 369
3–5 .. 337

Males:
6–11 .. 386
12–19 .. 400
20–29 .. 255
30–39 .. 202
40–49 .. 168
50–59 .. 151
60–69 .. 160
70+ .. 193

Females:
6–11 .. 331
12–19 .. 245
20–29 .. 172
30–39 .. 172
40–49 .. 124
50–59 .. 148
60–69 .. 154
70+ .. 180

Whole ▭   Lowfat/skim ▬

Grams, by sex and age (years)

TABLE 2

Beverage intakes: Average intake* per individual per day and percent of individuals using at least once in 3 days, 1977-78 and 1989-90

Beverage	Average intake (grams)		Percent using	
	1977-78	1989-90	1977-78	1989-90
Fluid milk	254	230	81	79
Whole	128	87	47	37
Lowfat/skim	66	137	24	48
Citrus juices	52	53	39	35
Noncitrus juices, nectars	12	22	10	15
Coffee	265	244	51	47
Tea	123	111	39	32
Fruit drinks and ades	50	53	24	24
Low-calorie	2	11	1	5
Soft drinks	141	238	52	63
Low-calorie	20	62	8	20

* Average per individual, whether or not the individual used food from the group. Average intakes per user would be higher.

Nearly all groups of teenagers and adults in the 1989-90 survey had calcium intakes below their Recommended Dietary Allowances (RDA), and the average calcium intake for women age 20 and over was 66 percent of the RDA. Milk and milk products are the major sources of calcium for Americans. However, intakes of carbonated soft drinks for teenagers and adults under 60 years of age were about equal to or higher than intakes of fluid milk.

The large increases in the share of milk intakes that were lowfat or skim and in the share of soft drinks that were low-calorie suggest that people are interested in limiting calories, fat, and sugar. Any of those interests could be satisfied by continuing to increase intakes of lowfat or skim milk and milk products, which would result in higher calcium intakes as well.

Fats, Oils, and Sweets Group

In 1989-90, total fat provided 35 percent of calories, and saturated fat provided 12 percent. Cholesterol intakes averaged 259 milligrams (mg).

The 1990 Dietary Guidelines for Americans recommend that individuals have a total fat intake of no more than 30 percent of calories and a saturated fat intake of less than 10 percent of calories. Many health authorities recommend a cholesterol intake of less than 300 mg daily.

The percentages of calories from total fat and saturated fat differ little by sex and age, by income, and by race. Cholesterol intakes are considerably higher for men than for women. Among men, average cholesterol intakes ranged from 296 mg for men age 70 and over to 365 mg for men 20 to 29 years old.

Americans got less energy from fat and more from carbohydrate in 1989-90 than in 1977-78 (fig. 3). Factors contributing to the reduced percentage of energy from fat include changes in the food available, such as more lower-fat products and leaner meats; changes in food choices, such as the shift from whole to lowfat and skim milk; and the increased use of foods high in carbohydrate, such as grain products and sweetened beverages.

Energy and Nutrients

On average, the food eaten in the 3 days of the survey provided consumers with 1,763 calories per day. As expected, men eat more than women: The average food energy intake in 1989-90 was 2,119 calories for men 20 and

FIGURE 3

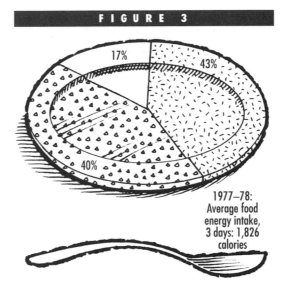

1977–78:
Average food energy intake, 3 days: 1,826 calories

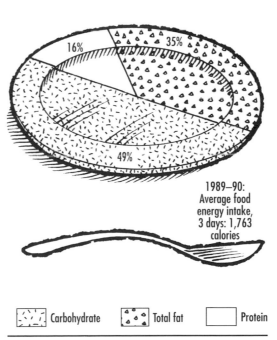

1989–90:
Average food energy intake, 3 days: 1,763 calories

Carbohydrate   Total fat   Protein

Food energy from protein, fat, and carbohydrate intake per individual per day, 3 days, 1977-78 and 1989-90

Nutrient intake compared with RDA: Women and men 20-29 years, 3 days, 1989-90

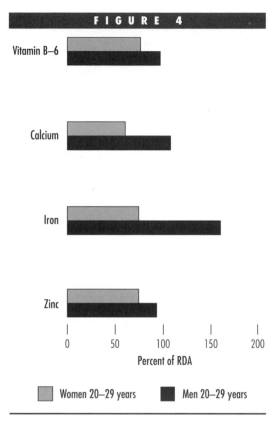

FIGURE 4

Vitamin B–6

Calcium

Iron

Zinc

0   50   100   150   200

Percent of RDA

☐ Women 20–29 years   ■ Men 20–29 years

over and 1,492 calories for women 20 and over. Energy intakes peaked at about 2,457 calories for males 12 to 29 years then declined progressively in older groups. Among females, energy intakes peaked at 1,688 calories for 6- to 11-year-olds then declined. For most age groups, calorie levels are slightly lower than they were in 1977-78.

The average energy intake in the low-income group was 1,610 calories, versus 1,773 calories in the middle-income group and 1,839 calories in the high-income group. The average

energy intake was slightly lower for blacks (1,714 calories) than for whites (1,773 calories).

For nearly all age, income, and race groups, the reported energy levels are below the average energy allowances recommended in the 10th edition of the Recommended Dietary Allowances (RDA). However, there is some evidence that people in nutrition surveys underreport the food they eat, either by completely omitting food items or by underestimating the amount eaten. Also, the average energy allowances are designed for a light-to-moderate level of physical activity. It is possible that Americans' actual level of physical activity is lower than light-to-moderate.

Intakes of some nutrients are below the RDA. Average nutrient intakes for most groups exceed the RDA for protein, vitamin A, vitamin C, thiamin, riboflavin, niacin, folate, vitamin B-12, and phosphorus. For some nutrients—vitamin E, vitamin B-6, calcium, magnesium, iron, and zinc—intakes were below the RDA for many groups. In 1977-78, intakes of vitamin B-6, calcium, magnesium, and iron were below the 1980 RDA for many groups; vitamin E and zinc were not examined in the 1977-78 survey (see chapter on "Making Healthy Food Choices" for a list of foods that contain nutrients that are below the RDA for many population groups).

For those nutrients below the RDA, intakes were lower for women than for men age 20 to 29 (fig. 4), as they were in nearly all age groups. For three nutrients—vitamin B-6, calcium, and zinc—average intakes were below the RDA regardless of income, but intakes were lower for low-income than for high-income individuals. Average calcium intake as a percentage of the RDA varied by race and was much lower for blacks (75 percent of RDA) than for whites (91 percent of RDA). Vitamin B-6 and zinc intakes were similar for blacks and whites, although both races had intakes below the RDA.

An average intake below the RDA does not necessarily mean that people in a group were malnourished. Individuals' nutrient requirements differ, and the RDA are set high enough to meet the requirements of nearly all healthy individuals. Thus, the RDA exceed the requirements of many individuals. However, the risk that some individuals have inadequate intakes increases as the average intake for the group falls further below the RDA.

More than one-fourth of the population consumed no fruit or fruit juice in 3 consecutive days in 1989-90. These individuals had average intakes of vitamins A and C that, when expressed as percentages of the RDA, were 38 to 70 percentage points below those of the population as a whole. Among people who consumed no fruit or fruit juice in 3 days, several age groups of women had intakes that were below RDA for vitamin A. For example, women 20 to 29 years who ate no fruit in 3 days had an average intake of vitamin A that was 74 percent of the RDA. Vitamin C intakes met the RDA for most groups of children, teenagers, and young men who ate no fruit in 3 days. However, men 70 and over had a vitamin C intake that was 69 percent of the RDA, and women 20 and over had vitamin C intakes that ranged from 67 to 81 percent of the RDA. Individuals who consumed no fruit in 3 days and who also indicated they did not have enough food to eat had an average vitamin C intake that was 82 percent of the RDA. Individuals who ate no fruit in 3 days also had a higher percentage of calories from fat (37 percent) than did all individuals (35 percent).

Calcium intakes are below the RDA for many population groups; women age 20 and over, for example, have intakes that range from 66 to 81 percent of the RDA. Calcium intakes are even lower for the more than one-fourth of women age 20 and over who drank no fluid milk in 3 days. For these women, calcium intakes ranged from 45 to 54 percent of the RDA. Calcium intakes by men age 20 and over who drank no milk in 3 days ranged from 54 to 70 percent of the RDA. The calcium intake for teenage girls in the general population was 65 percent of the RDA; in contrast, teenage girls who drank no milk in 3 days had an average calcium intake that was only 34 percent of the RDA.

Making Healthy Food Choices: Why People Eat What They Do, and What They Should Eat

Carole A. Davis
Joanne F. Guthrie
Anne Shaw
Linda Cleveland
Alyson J. Escobar
Lois Fulton
and
Susan Welsh
Human Nutrition
Information Service,
USDA, Hyattsville, MD

Progress has been made in planning meals as well as eating foods that are more in line with the Dietary Guidelines, but a great deal of education is still necessary.

Progress has been made in planning meals as well as eating foods that are more in line with the Dietary Guidelines for Americans (see illustration on next page). However, a great deal of education is still necessary.

What Do Americans Know and Believe About Nutrition?

Misconceptions, confusion, and lack of motivation were found to be barriers to dietary change by the USDA Diet and Health Knowledge Survey, which started in 1989, a follow-up to the department's food consumption survey (described in the previous chapter, "Diets of Americans").

Together, the two surveys can be used to determine how peoples' attitudes and knowledge about healthy eating influence their food choices and, as a result, their nutrient intakes.

The knowledge survey asks household meal planners about their attitudes toward the Dietary Guidelines, their perceptions of how their diets follow the guidelines, and their knowledge about how to follow the guidelines.

The conclusion is that many Americans don't understand—and to some degree don't care—what they're eating.

Ken Hammond/USDA 92BW1984

Lack of Awareness

While meal planners seemed to know that what they eat can affect their health, they don't really know why.

Almost ninety percent of meal planners agreed with the statement: "What you eat can make a big difference in your chance of getting a disease, like heart disease or cancer." But fewer knew how health problems are related to specific nutrients. More than 80 percent of respondents knew about health problems related to sodium and cholesterol, and 75 percent knew about health problems related to how much fat a person eats. Fewer still—65 percent or less—were aware of health problems related to saturated fat, calcium, fiber, and iron.

Lack of Motivation

Meal planners were asked how important it was to them personally to follow each of the Dietary Guidelines. Although many considered it important to "avoid too much fat," about one in eight meal planners rated this guideline of low importance.

Meal planners also were asked to rate the importance of "eating a variety of foods," of "eating at least five servings a day of fruits and vegetables," and of "eating at least six servings a day of breads, cereals and other grain products." (These servings of fruits, vegetables, and grains are the minimum amounts suggested in the Food Guide Pyramid.) Meal planners placed a lot of importance on "variety" but less importance on eating the numbers of servings recommended in the Food

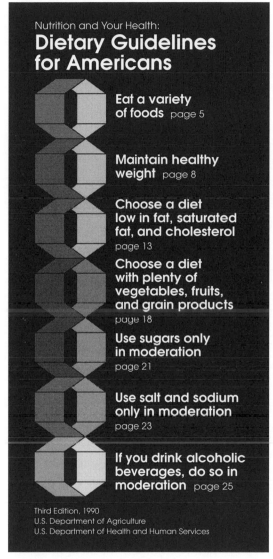

Nutrition and Your Health:
Dietary Guidelines for Americans

Eat a variety of foods page 5

Maintain healthy weight page 8

Choose a diet low in fat, saturated fat, and cholesterol page 13

Choose a diet with plenty of vegetables, fruits, and grain products page 18

Use sugars only in moderation page 21

Use salt and sodium only in moderation page 23

If you drink alcoholic beverages, do so in moderation page 25

Third Edition, 1990
U.S. Department of Agriculture
U.S. Department of Health and Human Services

Guide. About one-fourth of survey participants said that it was of low importance to them personally to eat at least five servings a day of fruits and vegetables.

Meal planners placed a lot of importance on "variety" but less importance on eating the numbers of servings recommended in the Food Guide.

Keith Weller/USDA 92CS0485

Inaccurate Perceptions

People's perceptions about their diets don't always match reality. For example, about 40 percent of main meal planners responding to the knowledge survey thought their diets were "about right" in terms of fat. But only about one-fourth had fat intakes that met the Dietary Guideline to limit fat intake to 30 percent of calories or less. Similarly, for saturated fat, about 50 percent of meal planners thought their diets were "about right." But, fewer than 25 percent reported intakes that met the Guideline to limit saturated fat intake to less than 10 percent of calories.

Lack of Knowledge

The last barrier to dietary change is lack of knowledge about how to put the Guidelines into action. In recent research, consumers expressed an interest in nutrition and some understanding of the health benefits of following the Dietary Guidelines, but said they found it difficult to "put it all together." They need "how-to" information that shows practical ways to eat healthfully. Knowledge about nutrients in foods and about how to plan for variety in the diet may help.

There is also confusion about which of the many different sources of nutrition information consumers should trust. They say they get conflicting advice and don't know whom to believe.

The Food Guide Pyramid

USDA has offered dietary guidance since the beginning of the century and the development of food guides was the way nutritional science was first translated into practical eating plans.

The first USDA food guide was developed in 1916. Other familiar food guides were the "Basic-7" developed in the 1940's and the "Basic-4" from the 1950's.

As more was learned about the relationship between diet and health, the focus shifted from concerns about nutritional adequacy to concerns about overconsumption. In 1980, USDA and the Department of Health and Human Services jointly issued seven principles for a healthful diet known as the Dietary Guidelines for Americans. Since then, the

---

Examples of good food sources* of nutrients that tend to be low in American diets

Vitamin B6	Banana, watermelon, fortified cereals, white potatoes with skin, sweet potatoes, chicken breast half or leg, turkey, beef, pork, fish, and liver.
Calcium	Yogurt, frozen yogurt, milk, cheese, tofu made with calcium sulfate, and cooked broccoli, spinach, and turnip greens.
Iron	Beef, dark turkey, cooked clams, oysters, and mussels, cooked soybeans and lentils, roasted pumpkin or squash seeds, dried apricots, and cooked spinach.
Magnesium	Whole-grain cereals, cooked dry beans, tofu made with magnesium chloride (nigari), nuts, roasted pumpkin or squash seeds, peanut butter, cooked oysters and scallops, and cooked spinach, broccoli, chard, and green lima beans.
Zinc	Yogurt, fortified ready-to-eat cereals, cooked oysters, crab, lobster, and mussels, beef, pork, lamb, and veal, turkey, liver, and roasted pumpkin or squash seeds.

*Contains at least 10 percent of the U.S. Recommended Daily Allowance (Daily Value) in a serving. Sources listed for each nutrient contain more of the nutrient in a serving than other commonly eaten foods.

Guidelines have been revised and reissued twice and a new review will start soon.

Work soon began on a new food guide to help people apply the guidelines to their daily food choices. Following an assessment of the professional community, it was determined that the new food guide should:

- Promote overall health (not be limited to a single disease),
- Be based on up-to-date research,
- Address the total diet (take into account competing concerns about nutritional adequacy and overconsumption),
- Be useful to the target audience,
- Be realistic (have nutritional goals met by commonly used foods),
- Be flexible (allow consumer choice in sources of fat, etc., within the limits of the total diet),
- Be practical (meet the needs of healthy people age 2 and over), and
- Be evolutionary (anticipate future dietary recommendations without major revision).

The nutritional goals for the food guide were based on the Recommended Dietary Allowances (RDA) and the Dietary Guidelines. The goals for vitamins and minerals were 100 percent of the RDA for various sex and age groups; nutrients that tend to be low in the American diet were given primary consideration. The goal for fat in the diet is no more than 30 percent of calories, with less than 10 percent of calories from saturated fatty acids.

Foods were categorized into groups based on their nutrient content, their use in meals, and how they have been grouped in past food guides. For example, dry beans and peas were included in the meat group because they are good sources of some of the nutrients for which meat is important—iron, zinc, and B vitamins. In addition, they are commonly used in meals as a lowfat, low cholesterol alternative to meat. And, traditionally, food guides have included beans and peas in the meat group.

The food groups identified for the new food guide were similar to the Basic Four, which had been used since the 1950's, with a few exceptions. Foods high in fat or added sugars with few other nutrients were put into a separate group. Vegetables and fruits also were separated to give them added emphasis and reflect their different usage. Subgroups were used to give emphasis to nutrients of concern, such as whole-grain products.

Four factors were considered in assigning serving sizes: typical servings or portion sizes; ease of use (for example, household units that

> ## Food Groups: Serving Sizes
>
> **Bread, cereal, rice and pasta**
> 1 slice of bread
> 1 ounce of ready-to-eat cereal
> 1/2 cup of cooked cereal, rice, or pasta
>
> **Vegetable**
> 1 cup of raw leafy vegetables
> 1/2 cup of other vegetables, cooked or chopped raw
> 3/4 cup of vegetable juice
>
> **Fruit**
> 1 medium apple, banana, orange
> 1/2 cup of chopped, cooked, or canned fruit
> 3/4 cup of fruit juice
>
> **Milk, yogurt, and cheese**
> 1 cup of milk or yogurt
> 1-1/2 ounces of natural cheese
> 2 ounces of process cheese
>
> **Meat, poultry, fish, dry beans, eggs, and nuts**
> 2-3 ounces of cooked lean meat, poultry, or fish
> 1/2 cup of cooked dry beans, 1 egg, or 2 tablespoons of peanut butter count as 1 ounce of meat (1/3 serving)

could easily be multiplied or divided were used); similar nutrient content (for example, 1/2 cup cooked vegetable provides about the same amount of nutrients as 1 cup leafy raw vegetable); tradition (for example, one slice of bread was the serving unit used in Basic 7 and Basic 4 food guides). No serving sizes were specified for fats, oils, and sweets because the message is to use them sparingly.

Food group servings for mixed foods like pizza or beef stew can be estimated based on the main ingredients and the amount eaten. For example, with a generous serving of pizza, the crust counts as a bread—possibly several servings. Pizza could also contribute whole or part servings of meat (ground beef, pepperoni), milk (cheese), and vegetable (tomato sauce, peppers, etc.). A helping of beef stew would count in the meat group and the vegetable group. Both pizza and beef stew have some fat—fat in the cheese on the pizza and in the gravy from the stew, if it is made from meat drippings.

In developing the food guide, each food group was assigned a nutrient profile—quantities of nutrients that one would expect to obtain on average from a serving. The relative popularity of foods within the group was taken into account. Therefore, the nutrient profile of a food group most often reflects the nutrient content of the foods most frequently consumed. For the grain, vegetable, fruit, milk, and meat groups, only foods in their lowest fat form without added sugars were included. This approach was consistent with the goal of allowing consumers maximum flexibility in choosing the sources of fat and added sugars they prefer.

Using the nutrient profiles of the food groups, the number of servings needed to meet the goals for vitamins and minerals was determined. Ranges in servings were used to cover the varying needs of males and females

TABLE 1			
Sample diets for a day at three calorie levels			
Calorie level	Lower about 1,600	Moderate about 2,200	Higher about 2,800
		Servings	
Bread group	6	9	11
Vegetable group	3	4	5
Fruit group	2	3	4
Milk group	2-3*	2-3*	2-3*
Meat group (ounces)	5	6	7
Total fat (grams)	53	73	93
Total added sugars (teaspoons)	6	12	18

* Women who are pregnant or breastfeeding, teenagers, and young adults to age 24 need 3 servings.

2 years and older. Once protein, vitamin, and mineral needs were met from foods in their lowest fat form without added sugars, fat was added up to the limit of 30 percent of calories; then the balance in calories was provided by added sugars. Analysis of the Food Guide showed that goals for adequacy and moderation were generally met. Iron, however, remained a concern for individuals who have high iron needs (menstruating, pregnant, and lactating women) and low calorie diets (1,600 calories). This problem may be addressed by selecting foods high in iron such as fortified breakfast cereals or through the use of iron supplements, if medically recommended.

Although the new Food Guide has been

The Food Guide Pyramid has been used extensively by the media, educators, nutrition and health professionals, and the food industry.

Ken Hammond/USDA 93CN0715-29

used in USDA publications since the mid-1980's, it was not well known. Therefore, in 1988, work began on a consumer booklet devoted entirely to the Food Guide and including a graphic illustration of the Food Guide. As a result, a booklet and a pyramid design evolved which were thought to convey the three key messages—variety, proportionality, and moderation.

Variety among food groups was shown by the names of the groups and by the separate sections of the pyramid. Variety within food groups was shown by the pictures of food.

Proportionality was conveyed by the size of the food group sections and the text indicating numbers of servings. **Moderation** of foods high in fat and added sugars was shown by the small size of the tip of the pyramid and the "use sparingly" text. Moderation related to food choices within food groups was shown by the density of the fat and added sugars symbols in the food groups. It was anticipated that the latter message would be more difficult to communicate without text.

The Food Guide Pyramid has been used extensively by the media, educators, nutrition and health professionals, and the food industry. It is expected that this food guide will be

18

revised as the science base evolves. But it is unlikely that the underlying themes of variety, proportionality, and moderation initiated in USDA about 100 years ago will change.

Making the Pyramid Fit the Family
The Dietary Guidelines are for all Americans 2 years of age and older.

Young Children
Infants and toddlers have special dietary needs because of their rapid growth and development. A health care provider should be consulted for advice on feeding them.

As young children begin to eat with the family, usually about the age of 2 or older, they should be encouraged to choose diets that are lower in fat and saturated fat and that provide the calories and nutrients they need for normal growth. Young children can be served the same variety of foods as everyone else, but in smaller amounts to suit their smaller needs—a 1/4 to 1/3 cup portion of vegetable, for example. They should have at least the equivalent of 2 cups of milk each day, but they can have it in several small portions. Because young children often eat only a small amount at one time, they can be offered nutritious "meal foods" as snacks—milk or fruit juice, cut-up fruit, vegetable sticks, strips of cooked meat or poultry, whole-grain crackers and peanut butter, half a sandwich.

School Age Children
Calorie needs vary widely for elementary school children. They should eat at least the

Ken Hammond/92CN0760-27

All teenagers and young adults to age 24 should have three servings of milk, yogurt, or cheese daily to meet their calcium needs.

lower numbers of servings from each of the five major food groups daily. However, many will need more calories for growth and activity, so larger portions of foods from the major food groups should be served and simple, nutritious snacks added. Foods from the Pyramid tip, such as candies and soft drinks, should be used sparingly. Fruit juice or lowfat milk should be served instead of soft drinks. Juice can be diluted with extra water or sparkling water to satisfy thirst on hot days.

Many children gain unwanted weight due to sedentary lifestyles. All children should be encouraged to participate in physically active outdoor play to promote strength and fitness. Active children tend to grow into active adults, and parents who are active are more likely to have active children.

Teens and Young Adults
All teenagers and young adults to age 24 should have three servings of milk, yogurt, or cheese daily to meet their calcium needs.

Adults should have at least the lower number of servings from each food group.

Bob Nichols/USDA 93BW1166-22

Research has shown that bone density increases well into the twenties. Eating foods that provide adequate calcium to attain maximum bone density is important in helping prevent development of osteoporosis and bone fractures in later life. Yet most teenagers, especially teen girls, do not eat the recommended amounts of milk, yogurt, or cheese. For many teens, especially older teens and young adults, soft drinks have replaced milk as a beverage. If they don't drink milk, teens should include lowfat yogurts and lowfat cheeses as calcium sources. Dark-green leafy vegetables also supply calcium, but in much smaller amounts per serving than dairy products.

Most teenage boys can eat the higher number of servings from each food group. Teenage girls usually need more food than the lower number of servings, especially when they are active or growing rapidly. Teen girls who are active in vigorous sports may need the higher number of servings. They should increase their servings from the five major food groups, and go easy on foods from the Pyramid tip—fats, oils, and sweets. Physical activity should be used to control weight rather than repeated dieting. Choosing lowfat foods is a good way to cut calories without cutting vitamins and minerals important for growth and development.

Adults

Adults should have at least the lower number of servings from each food group. With a moderate amount of fat and sugars, this number of servings provides about 1,600 calories—about the right amount for a sedentary woman and some older adults. However, most adults will need more calories than this, depending on body size and physical activity. Most men can have the middle to upper number of servings in the ranges. The lower to middle numbers of servings in the ranges are more appropriate for most women.

Most adults do not get the recommended two servings from the milk, yogurt, and cheese group, and thus do not meet the recommendations for calcium. Like teenagers and young adults, they report drinking soft drinks, coffee, or tea more often than milk. Nonfat and lowfat milks and yogurts provide the most calcium with the least fat and calories. Milk in soups and simple puddings, or lowfat cheese in pizza and casserole dishes can be used to increase servings from the milk group. Lower fat dairy desserts such as ice milk or frozen yogurt can also count toward servings from this food group, but these foods have more calories from the added sugars.

Most adults do not get recommended amounts of fruits and vegetables, averaging less than the suggested total of "five a day" from both groups. Fruit is particularly underconsumed. Only a little more than half the people surveyed reported eating fruit on any given day.

Whole fruit as a snack, as well as cut-up fruit in salad, or as an accent in a main dish, or baked for dessert, can increase fruit intake.

Although most people report eating vegetables more often than fruit, much of the vegetables consumed are potatoes, especially french fries. A greater variety of vegetables, especially dark-green leafy vegetables and cooked dry beans and peas, should be included.

Most adults need to eat less fat and fatty foods to keep fat in their total diet at the recommended level of 30 percent or less of calories. Choosing more grain products, vegetables, and fruit, and picking lower fat meats and dairy products more often, can help lower fat and calorie intake. Salad dressings, mayonnaise, butter, and margarine should be used sparingly.

Weight control is a major nutrition concern for many adults. Total food intake is most important in weight control, but increasing physical activity helps. Regular exercise allows adults to eat more food to get the nutrients they need without gaining unwanted weight. It is also important in helping them to maintain fitness.

Pregnant and Breastfeeding Women

Women who are pregnant or breastfeeding have higher needs for many vitamins and minerals to support the growth and development of their babies. Most of these needs can be met with foods in a healthy diet, but a physician may prescribe a multivitamin and mineral supplement as well.

Pregnant or breastfeeding women should

have at least three servings of milk, yogurt, or cheese daily to meet their calcium needs. They should eat more breads and cereals, fruits, vegetables, meat, poultry, fish, dry beans, eggs, and nuts, too—most need about the middle numbers of servings in the ranges from each food group.

There are many reasons for mothers to breastfeed their babies. Breastmilk provides just the right balance of vitamins, minerals, and other important nutrients needed by babies, and is easily digested. Breastmilk helps fight infections and prevent allergies, so breastfed babies tend to be sick less often. Breastfeeding is good for the mother, too. It helps mothers' bodies return to normal after pregnancy. Breastmilk is low-cost and convenient, always warm and ready-to-feed.

Older Adults

Older people vary in their dietary needs. Some eat like younger adults, and others eat relatively little food. Older people need to eat foods from each of the five major food groups daily, but less of foods in the Pyramid tip. The lowest numbers of servings in the ranges are about right for many older women; the middle numbers of servings are right for many older men.

Many older people eat less than recommended amounts from the milk, yogurt, and cheese group. Although they eat more fruits and vegetables than other age groups, they fall short of recommended amounts from these food groups as well. Eating plenty of vegetables, fruits, and whole-grain products,

drinking plenty of liquids, and getting regular exercise can help prevent the constipation that troubles many older adults. For those who have difficulty chewing, cooked vegetables and fruits can provide dietary fiber, as can cooked cereals and baked goods that contain whole grains.

Regular physical activity is an important part of a healthy lifestyle for older adults. Regular exercise can improve the functioning of the heart and lungs, increase strength and flexibility, and contribute to a feeling of well-being. Moderate exercise that places weight on the bones, such as walking, helps maintain and possibly increase bone strength in older adults—to help prevent disabling fractures.

Many older adults take several medications. It's important to find out from the doctor or pharmacist if these medicines are affected by food or beverages, or if there are any special instructions about diet or foods to avoid when taking the medicine.

Planning Menus

Variety and balance are the keys to menu planning. Planning ahead saves time, effort, and money, and it helps increase variety and balance in the diet.

The Food Guide Pyramid can be used to choose a varied and nutritious diet.

- Choose foods daily from each of the five major food groups—breads, cereals, rice, and pasta; fruits; vegetables; meats, poultry, fish, dry beans and peas, eggs, and nuts; and milk, yogurt, and cheese.
- Include different types of foods from within

Examples of foods that have been prepared with and without extra fat

Lower	Calories	Fat (grams)	Higher	Calories	Fat (grams)
Baked potato, 1 med.	120	1	French fries, 14	225	14
Whole-wheat bread 1 slice	60	1	Croissant, 1 medium	230	12
Baked chicken, without skin 3 ounces	160	6	Fried chicken, with skin 3 ounces	220	11
Broccoli, steamed 1/2 cup	25	0	Broccoli with cheese sauce, 1/2 cup	111	7

the groups because specific foods differ in the kinds and amounts of nutrients they provide. For example, include in a week's menu red meats (like beef and pork), poultry, and fish. Pick different breads, fruits, and vegetables as well—especially dark-green leafy vegetables, dry beans and peas, and whole-grain breads and cereals; these foods provide dietary fiber and nutrients that are low in many diets.

- Choose several servings of whole-grain products each day, and include dark-green, deep-yellow, and starchy vegetables, as well as other vegetables, regularly. Include dark-green leafy vegetables and

dry beans and peas several times a week—they are especially good sources of vitamins and minerals. Because dry beans and peas are low in fat but high in protein and in many of the vitamins and minerals provided by the meat group, they are good meat alternates as well as vegetable selections.

- Have at least the smaller number of servings suggested from each group. Limit the total amount of food eaten to maintain a healthy weight.
- You don't need to measure your servings—just use the amounts in the Food Serving Sizes Box (p. 16) as a general guide. If you

Whether menus are planned in advance or shopping is done just to restock shelves at home, the total diet should be considered before going to the store.

Ken Hammond/USDA 93BW1444-10

want to see how well you can estimate amounts, try measuring a few vegetables, or portions of cereal, rice, or pasta, to see what 1/2 cup looks like on your plate. A 3-ounce serving of cooked lean meat is about the size of a deck of cards.

Food Shopping

Whether menus are planned in advance or shopping is done just to restock shelves at home, the total diet should be considered before going to the store. Foods should be selected from all of the major food groups in the Food Guide Pyramid—breads, vegetables, fruits, milk products, and lean meats or dry beans. Foods that are lower in fat, added sugars, and sodium should be chosen most often.

Nutrition and ingredient labels on foods can be used to choose main ingredients and calorie, fat, and sodium content. Food labels can be used as guides to specific foods within each of the food groups presented in the Pyramid. For example, people trying to eat more servings from the bread, cereal, rice, and pasta group, but also watching their weight and trying to get more fiber in their diet, can use food labels to help them find a breakfast cereal that's a good source of fiber without extra calories from added fats and sugars.

Here are some ways to get variety in the diet while watching fat, saturated fat, cholesterol, and sodium intake:

Breads, cereals, rice, and pasta:
- whole-wheat, rye, pumpernickel, mixed grain, and enriched breads and rolls, bagels, and english muffins
- whole-grain crackers, such as graham crackers, wheat crackers, and rice cakes
- whole-grain breakfast cereals
- plain rice, pasta (cooked with less salt)

Fruit:
- fresh fruit
- canned fruit in juice rather than heavy syrup
- canned or frozen fruit juice, unsweetened

Vegetables:
- fresh leafy vegetables and other vegetables
- frozen vegetables without sauce
- canned vegetables, tomato sauces, and soups—try those that have reduced sodium, or no salt added, if available
- dry beans or split peas, canned beans, bean and pea soups—look for lower sodium versions

Meat, poultry, fish, dry beans, eggs, nuts:
- fresh, well-trimmed, lean meats—beef round, loin, sirloin, chuck arm; pork loin, roasts, and chops; leg of lamb. One pound

---

Moderating Fat: A Balancing Act

Even favorite foods that may be higher in fat can fit into an eating plan that provides a total diet low in fat. For example:

- If you drink a serving of whole milk rather than skim, leave out 2 teaspoons of fat elsewhere in the day's meals. For instance, skip the sour cream or butter on a baked potato.

- If you want fried chicken, have lowfat foods to go with it—green salad with a fat-free dressing, rather than creamy salads such as potato salad or macaroni salad. Or choose lowfat foods at other meals.

- Eat less of a high-fat choice, or eat it less often. Or choose a lower fat alternative, such as frozen yogurt instead of ice cream.

---

of trimmed boneless raw meat will make about four 3-ounce cooked servings.
- lean ground beef—ask the butcher to trim fat off and grind a piece of beef round steak
- fresh chicken and turkey parts—boneless, skinless breasts or thighs
- fresh or plain frozen fish, tuna fish canned in water

Milk, yogurt, cheese:
- lowfat (1 or 2 percent) or skim milk
- lowfat or nonfat yogurt, plain or flavored
- part-skim and lowfat cheeses such as moz-

zarella, ricotta, cottage cheese
- frozen yogurt or ice milk

Spreads and seasonings:
- margarine, with liquid vegetable oil listed as the first ingredient
- vegetable oils, such as canola, olive, corn, and soybean oils, for cooking and salad dressings
- reduced-calorie mayonnaise and salad dressing
- salt-free herb blends for seasoning

Preparing Foods

While foods as purchased may be low in calories, fat, and sodium, whether they stay low depends on what is added during home preparation, what cooking procedures are used, and what extras are added at the table. There are ways to cut fat, added sugars, and sodium, and to increase dietary fiber when preparing foods. Even if food is not usually prepared at home, these tips will be helpful in choosing wisely among the foods offered in cafeterias, restaurants, and dining halls.

Cutting Fat
- Choose lean cuts of meat and trim fat from meat before or after cooking. Remove skin from poultry before or after cooking.
- Brown ground meats without added fat. Drain off fat before mixing in the other ingredients.
- Roast, bake, broil, or simmer meat, poultry, or fish rather than frying.

- Cook meat or poultry on a rack so fat will drain off.
- Chill meat or poultry broth until the fat becomes solid; spoon off the fat before using the broth.
- Extend meat, poultry, or fish in main dishes and casseroles by combining with pasta, rice, other grains, or vegetables.
- Use cooked dry beans and peas as meat alternates occasionally.
- Steam, boil, bake, or microwave vegetables rather than frying them. Or stirfry them in just a small amount of vegetable oil.
- Season vegetables with herbs and spices rather than with fatty sauces, butter, or margarine. Try flavored vinegars, lemon juice, or reduced-calorie dressings on salads.
- Replace whole milk with lowfat or skim milk in puddings, soups, and baked products. Substitute plain yogurt or blender-whipped lowfat cottage cheese for sour cream or mayonnaise.

Reducing Added Sugars
- Reduce the amount of sugar in baked goods you prepare. Use 1/2 cup of sugar per cup of flour in cakes; 1 tablespoon of sugar per cup of flour in muffins and quick breads. Serve fruit quick bread instead of cake for dessert.
- Bake or broil fruits for a dessert, garnish, or appetizer.
- Experiment with spices such as cinnamon, cardamom, coriander, nutmeg, ginger, and mace to enhance the sweet flavor of foods. Spiced foods will taste sweeter if warmed.

- Use a lightly sweetened fruit sauce in place of frosting on cake, or add the sauce to plain yogurt instead of buying a commercial fruit yogurt with more added sugars.
- Try a fruit juice cooler made from any combination of fruit juices with club soda, mineral water, or seltzer water instead of a soft drink or sweetened fruit drink.

Cutting sodium

- Cook rice, pasta, and hot cereals without salt or with less salt than the package calls for (try 1/8 teaspoon of salt for two servings).
- Experiment with the flavors of lemon or lime juice, herbs, and spices as seasonings for vegetables and meats instead of salt. Start with 1/8 teaspoon of dried herbs or spices for four servings, then let your taste guide you.
- Adjust your recipes, gradually cutting down on the amount of salt. If some of the ingredients already contain salt, such as cured meats, canned soup, canned vegetables or cheese, additional salt is not needed. Often using a no-salt-added canned product plus a small amount of salt results in a dish with less sodium than a regular salted canned product and no additional salt.

- Limit the sodium-containing condiments used in cooking or at the table, such as salt, flavored salts, soy sauce, dill pickles, salad dressings, and sauces. Look for lower sodium versions of sauces and dressings.

Increasing Dietary Fiber

- Choose cereals and baked goods made with whole grains.
- Try whole-grain flours in pancakes, muffins, and quick breads. Add fruit, such as dried apricots, raisins, bananas, berries, or apples.
- Eat fruits and vegetables with their peels—apples, pears, peaches, summer squash, or potatoes.
- Add cooked, canned, or dry beans, split peas, and lentils to your favorite soups, stews, and salads. If traditional foods that are important to your cultural and ethnic heritage are high in fat or sodium, you can often find lower fat and lower sodium versions.

To order a single copy of "The Food Guide Pyramid" booklet, send a check or money order for $1.00 made out to Superintendent of Documents to: Consumer Information Center, Pueblo, Colorado 81009. Ask for item number 117-Z.

Using the New Nutrition Label To Make Choices

Danielle Schor
Public Affairs Specialist,
Food Safety and Inspection
Service, USDA,
Washington, DC,
and
Etta Saltos
Nutritionist, Human Nutrition
Information Service, USDA,
Hyattsville, MD

Helping consumers to choose more healthful foods has always been a priority at USDA. Since 1916, when the first food guide was published, Americans have depended on USDA for sound dietary advice. But putting that advice into practice hasn't always been easy. As more products appear on supermarket shelves, finding out what's in the food can be a challenge for consumers. Food labels provide helpful information, but confusing statements and incomplete information have frustrated consumers for years.

USDA/HNIS photo 8531

Since 1916, when the first food guide was published, Americans have depended on USDA for sound dietary advice.

The good news for consumers is that the new food label is here. USDA's Food Safety and Inspection Service (FSIS), which regulates meat and poultry safety and labeling, has worked closely with the Food and Drug Administration (FDA) of the U.S. Department of Health and Human Services (HHS), which regulates other foods, to develop one label that gives consumers the information they need to make healthy food choices. By the summer of 1994, most processed products—from frankfurters to frozen waffles—will be required to carry the new nutrition label. The new labels may appear on some products even sooner. A voluntary nutrition labeling program has been established for raw produce and raw meat, fish, and poultry. Even though nutrition labeling is voluntary for these foods, the program carries strong incentives for retailers to participate. Both USDA and FDA will study retailer participation to determine if the program should become mandatory.

Getting Here From There

Nutrition labeling is not new. For many years, manufacturers have been encouraged to provide nutrition information on food labels. Since 1973, FSIS has required nutrition information on labels when nutrition-related claims are made, for example about fat or sodium content. The current label reform effort began in 1989, when USDA and HHS jointly sponsored a study by the National Academy of Sciences to provide options for improving food labeling. In November 1991,

Lester Shephard/USDA 92BW1630-13

The Food Safety and Inspection Service (FSIS) has worked closely with the Food and Drug Administration (FDA) to develop one label that gives consumers the information they need to make good food choices. An FSIS compliance officer checks food labels at a supermarket.

FSIS issued a regulatory proposal for a mandatory nutrition labeling program for processed meat and poultry and voluntary guidelines for fresh meat and poultry products. FDA simultaneously proposed regulations on nutrition labeling for foods other than meat and poultry to comply with the Nutrition Labeling and Education Act of 1990. While FSIS was not required by this legislation to issue regulations for meat and poultry, the agency chose to initiate the requirement. After soliciting public input through hearings and comments in response to regulatory proposals, FSIS and FDA issued final nutrition labeling regulations on January 6, 1993.

Why the Changes?

The new nutrition label addresses today's public health priorities, in which conditions linked in part to diet, such as heart disease and some forms of cancer, have become much more prevalent than nutritional deficiency diseases of past generations, such as scurvy. The new label provides more specific information on fat, for instance, detailing how much saturated fat and cholesterol are in the product. It can be useful as a tool for nutrition education in combination with other efforts. The new label also provides food companies with an incentive to improve the nutritional quality of their products.

Nutrition Facts

Serving Size 1 cup (228g)
Servings Per Container 2

Amount Per Serving

Calories 260   Calories from Fat 120

% Daily Value*

Total Fat 13g	**20%**
Saturated Fat 5g	**25%**
Cholesterol 30mg	**10%**
Sodium 660mg	**28%**
Total Carbohydrate 31g	**10%**
Dietary Fiber 0g	**0%**
Sugars 5g	
Protein 5g	

Vitamin A 4%	•	Vitamin C 2%	
Calcium 15%	•	Iron 4%	

* Percent Daily Values are based on a 2,000 calorie diet. Your daily values may be higher or lower depending on your calorie needs:

	Calories:	2,000	2,500
Total Fat	Less than	65g	80g
Sat Fat	Less than	20g	25g
Cholesterol	Less than	300mg	300mg
Sodium	Less than	2,400mg	2,400mg
Total Carbohydrate		300g	375g
Dietary Fiber		25g	30g

Calories per gram:
Fat 9 • Carbohydrate 4 • Protein 4

What's New?

- Serving sizes are now more uniform for over 150 food categories, consistent across product lines, and closer to the amounts people actually eat. They also must be expressed in both metric measures and common household measures such as cups, pieces, or ounces.

- The list of nutrients identifies those that are essential to health and makes it easier for consumers to meet dietary recommendations and to determine how foods meet their own individual needs. Manufacturers are now required to list total calories, calories from fat, total fat, saturated fat, cholesterol, sodium, total carbohydrate, dietary fiber, sugars, protein, vitamin A, vitamin C, calcium, and iron. Other nutrients may be listed on a voluntary basis.

- The term "Daily Value" will be used to place the nutrition information on the label in the context of a total diet. These numbers provide guidance for the amount of each nutrient Americans should eat per day. Some are maximums, as with fat; others are recommended minimums, as with carbohydrates. The daily values are based on a daily diet of 2,000 calories, which is appropriate for most women, including teenage girls, and some sedentary men. The footnote provides daily values for a 2,500 calorie diet, which may be closer to what most men, teenage boys, and active women should consume. Individuals should adjust the values to fit their own caloric needs.

- Nutrient content claims such as "light" and "lean" have long been used on food labels, but their meanings have been vague. Now specific definitions for the following terms have been set: "free," "more," "low," "less," "reduced," "light," "high," and "good source of." Two additional nutrient content claims— "lean" and "extra lean"—are available for meat, poultry, fish, and game products.
- FDA is allowing health claims for seven relationships between a nutrient or food and the reduced risk of a disease or health-related condition. FSIS is studying the issue of health claims for meat and poultry products and will issue regulations in the future.

How To Use the New Label To Choose a Healthful Diet

The Dietary Guidelines suggest that you choose a diet low in fat, saturated fat, and cholesterol, moderate in sodium and sugar, and containing plenty of vegetables, fruits, and grain products. A few tips for using the new food labels to choose such a diet are provided below.

- Look for nutrient content claims such as "free," "low," or "reduced" on the front of the label to help identify foods which are low in calories, fat, saturated fat, cholesterol, and sodium. Claims such as "good source" and "high" can help you find foods that contain significant amounts of the dietary fiber, vitamins, and minerals that you need. However, you don't have to select only foods with these claims on the label. In moderation, all foods can fit into a healthful diet.

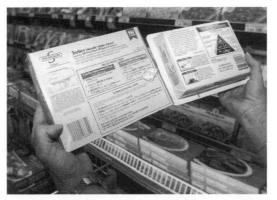

Ken Hammond/93BW1442-2

The new nutrition label provides food companies with an incentive to improve the nutritional quality of their products.

- The required nutrition information on the new labels can also help you find foods that are low in fat and saturated fat. The Dietary Guidelines suggest you eat a diet that provides 30 percent or fewer calories from fat and less than 10 percent of calories from saturated fat. Thus, the recommended upper limit on the grams of fat and saturated fat in your diet depends on the calories you need. The "% Daily Value" information listed on the label is based on an intake of 2,000 calories, which is about right for many women, teenage girls, and some sedentary men. If you fit into one of these categories, you can simply monitor the "% Daily Value" information from the foods you eat so the total is close to or less than 100% over the day.
- If you do not fit into one of these categories, you will need to determine your own target levels of fat and saturated fat depending on your caloric requirement. Target levels of fat and saturated fat intake

Take the time to read food labels. You'll find lots of new information that can help you plan a healthful diet.

USDA/0285X110-16A

TABLE 1

Target levels of total fat and saturated fat intake at different calorie levels

Calories	1,600	1,800	2,000*	2,200	2,500	2,800
Total fat (grams)	53	60	65	73	80	93
Saturated fat (grams)	18	20	20	24	25	31

* The figures for total fat and saturated fat at the 2,000 calorie level have been rounded for use on the nutrition label.

for several calorie levels are provided (see table 1). Many older adults, children, and sedentary women need fewer than 2,000 calories per day. Many teenage boys, most men, and active women need more than 2,000 calories per day. The actual amount of fat and saturated fat contained in one serving of a food are listed immediately after the nutrient name, such as "Total fat 13 g." Some people keep a running total of the amount of fat and saturated fat they eat in a day and compare it to their target level.

- The "% Daily Value" information may also be used to help you moderate your intake of sodium and cholesterol. The daily values for sodium (less than 2,400 mg) and cholesterol (less than 300 mg) are the same for everyone, so you do not have to make any adjustments based on your caloric needs.

Balance Is the Key

It's important to note that you don't have to completely avoid foods that are high in fat, saturated fat, cholesterol, and sodium. It's your average intake over a few days, not in a single food or even a single meal, that's important. For example, if you eat a high-fat food or meal, balance your intake by choosing low-fat foods the rest of the day or the next day. You can use food labels to help you plan meals and budget your intake of fat, saturated fat, cholesterol, and sodium over several days.

Take the time to read food labels. You'll find lots of new information that can help you plan a healthful diet.

Public Education

FSIS and FDA are working together with other Government agencies—including USDA's Human Nutrition Information Service, Food and Nutrition Service, and Extension Service—and a variety of professional, consumer, and trade associations to educate the public on the new nutrition label. A particular goal of the National Exchange for Food Labeling Education (NEFLE) is to see that as many Americans as possible learn to use the new label—particularly special populations such as older Americans, ethnic minorities, children, persons with special dietary needs, and persons with low reading skills.

A key feature of the Exchange is the USDA/FDA Food Labeling Education Information Center within the Food and Nutrition Information Center of USDA's National Agricultural Library. The Center maintains a database on consumer education projects and current research on label education. FSIS and FDA encourage educators to contact the Center before beginning projects, to seek possible partners and avoid duplication.

The label education effort has two phases. First, people need to become comfortable with the new label and terms. They can then learn how to use the label to choose a healthful diet. The Food and Drug Administration, in conjunction with FSIS, is preparing a brochure to help consumers understand the new label. Single copies are available from FDA, HF-E-88, Rockville, MD 20857, or from FSIS Publications, Room 1180-South, Washington, DC 20250.

The Human Nutrition Information Service is preparing two publications with more information on using the new food labels to choose a healthful diet. One publication is a comprehensive reference for professionals who write for consumers; the other is a brochure for consumers to use directly. For more information about either of these publications, write to: Nutrition Education Research Branch, Human Nutrition Information Service, U.S. Department of Agriculture, Federal Building, Room 353, 6505 Belcrest Rd., Hyattsville, MD 20782.

The following contacts can provide more information on the new nutrition label: your local county Cooperative Extension Service, State land-grant universities, the National Agricultural Library's Food Labeling Education Information Center, FDA regional public affairs specialists, FSIS's Office of Public Awareness (which includes USDA's Meat and Poultry Hotline, 1-800-535-4555), and HNIS's Nutrition Education Research Branch (address above).

Bringing Nutrition to Life in New York's Schools

Christine M. Olson
Professor, Division of
Nutritional Sciences, and
Assistant Dean for
Research and Graduate
Studies, College of
Human Ecology,
and
Patricia F. Thonney
Extension Associate,
Division of
Nutritional Sciences,
Cornell University,
Ithaca, NY

School-based nutrition education is a pivotal component of our Nation's strategy for health promotion. In 1991, the U.S. Department of Health and Human Services published Healthy People 2000: National Health Promotion and Disease Prevention Objectives. One health objective for the year 2000 was to "increase to at least 75 percent the proportion of the Nation's schools that provide nutrition education from preschool through 12th grade, preferably as part of quality school health education."

With the Food and Nutrition Service (FNS) and the Cooperative Extension System (CES) as partners, USDA is in a unique position to promote the nutritional well-being of the Nation's school children through nutrition education. The future health of our citizenry may depend on how well we do today in imparting a very basic life skill—eating to promote health and well-being—to our young people.

Partner Agencies

FNS administers the National School Lunch Program, begun in 1946, and the National School Breakfast Program. The school lunch program serves about 24 million children each school day, about half of them from low-income families. Its goal is to provide low-cost or free lunches as one way to safeguard the health and well-being of our Nation's children. FNS also administers the Nutrition Education and Training Program (NET), established by Congress in 1977 to enable teachers and school foodservice personnel to provide coordinated classroom and lunchroom experiences for effective nutrition education.

The CES includes an extensive network of educators in each land-grant university and nearly all 3,150 counties in the United States. As part of the land-grant system, CES professionals, paraprofessionals, and trained volunteers provide food and nutrition education to meet locally identified needs. CES has been a major and effective force in addressing the public's food and nutrition concerns.

The Gap Between Knowing and Doing

Childhood and adolescence are life stages marked by considerable change. Eating behaviors often reflect these physical, psychological, and social changes. For example, appetite fluctuations usually correspond to spurts and plateaus in growth; changes in food preferences may reflect an increasing need to assert independence or a response to new social and environmental situations. Nutrition and exercise patterns that are formed during the first two decades of life can shape an individual's health and well-being—now and in the future.

Recent surveys indicate that children and adolescents know a lot about nutrition. Yet this knowledge isn't necessarily translated into positive eating practices. To explain why they don't make positive health choices, adolescents often give reasons relating to lack of self-discipline and lack of a sense of urgency about diet and health. Many don't feel respon-

Ken Hammond/USDA 92CN0710-2

A teacher at Bailey's Elementary School in northern Virginia dines with her students as part of the nutrition education program to promote health and well being in our young people.

sible for their own food choices, explaining that they rely on adults to keep them healthy. As one student said, "When you're a kid, your parents, they always watch out for you and eating and stuff like that. When you're older, you're watching out for your own self and you're taking responsibility for you and other people won't."

New York Educators
Address the Challenge

The Nutrition for Life program illustrates one State's response to the challenge of school-

based nutrition education. New York State's successful program forged partnerships among CES, NET, the State departments of health and education, and industry.

"Nutrition is not peripheral to a child's learning. It is a basic skill, a basic need," says Matilda Cuomo, New York State's First Lady, who challenged educators to create a comprehensive school-based nutrition education program. Developed by CES faculty in the Division of Nutritional Sciences at Cornell University, the three integral components of Nutrition for Life are: (1) a comprehensive set of

Children know a lot about nutrition. In a northern Virginia supermarket, Delores Jones (left) shows her grandson Nick Stanko the nutritional benefits of the product she is purchasing.

Ken Hammond/USDA 92BW0796-26A

teaching materials for kindergarten through 12th grade (K-12), (2) a peer training team model for disseminating the materials and training local teachers, and (3) an evaluation plan for determining program effectiveness.

Teaching Materials

Nutrition for Life is helping thousands of students develop a basic life skill—eating to promote health and well-being. Learning experiences throughout the K-12 materials emphasize the importance of meeting nutrient

needs without excess fat, sugar, or sodium, concepts drawn from the Dietary Guidelines for Americans, which were jointly issued by USDA and the Department of Health and Human Services (HHS).

Elementary school children explore, experiment, and experience personal nutrition issues. For example, students learn to "Be A Choosy Chewer" by choosing good snacks and being physically active; science experiments in "The Nutrient Connection" reveal the relationship between what students eat and what happens inside their bodies; in "A Case of Waste," students examine the ecological consequences of food waste.

The seven segments of learning experiences provide opportunities to participate in interdisciplinary approaches to solving problems and making decisions. Not only do elementary school students learn important nutrition skills, but they also learn math by measuring and estimating; science by observing, comparing, classifying, inferring, and applying; language arts by reading, writing, analyzing, and interpreting; social studies by exploring people, places, and situations; and the arts through music, drama, drawing, and creative expression.

The 7th and 8th grade teaching materials complement New York State's curricula for Health and Home and Career Skills. Students examine nutrition problems and needs of people at different stages of the life cycle, explore influences on their personal food choices, and develop a personal contract for fitness. As one teacher described the materials, "It takes nutrition out of any kind of textbook and puts it into a context that the kids can see in their everyday lives and use."

At the senior high level, Nutrition for Life targets three groups of students. Students in health and physical education classes devise a program of physical activity and eating that will enable them to be personally fit. Students in home economics classes apply the options and control over time, money, skills, and ingredients when preparing foods that are consistent with the Dietary Guidelines. Preg-

nant and parenting teens acquire skills in making decisions that will positively affect their own and their babies' health. Through the use of participatory, real-life nutrition situations, high school students develop problem-solving, decision-making, and resource management skills as well as valuing the wise use of personal and community resources.

ALIVE! Food & Fitness for Life, an innovative magazine for high schoolers with a popular press style, integrates the three teaching units. Its goal is to motivate teenagers to learn about positive nutrition practices. Many teens consider nutrition boring, unimportant to their health now, and something that is more their parents' responsibility than their own. The 32-page, full-color magazine meets this challenge with its upbeat, positive tone to promote self-esteem, personal situations and experiences, and a contemporary, mature design. Personal interviews, soap-opera fiction, question and answer columns, and a peer advice column are used to engage the reader. The lead article features interviews with athletes to set the pace for this classroom magazine aimed at attracting both male and female readers.

Comments from classroom teachers, school psychologists, dietitians in private practice, 4-H leaders, church youth leaders, PTA presidents, and parents indicate that ALIVE! is being used effectively with teenagers in a variety of educational settings. One nutritionist said, "It's a good way to start conversations with my clients."

Senior high school students are given classes on nutritional values of food consistent with the Dietary Guidelines.

Ken Hammond/USDA 92BW1985

Peer Training Team Model

No matter how well developed a school-based program is, it will be successful only if it is effectively distributed and supported. This involves persuading a school system of the wisdom of adopting a program, training teachers in using the materials, and maintaining the quality of the program.

To meet this challenge in New York State, a peer training team model was adopted to distribute the 7th through 12th grade materials. A similar model had been used to effec-

tively distribute a newly mandated Home and Career Skills curriculum throughout the State. Fifteen training teams were formed, each including at least one representative of the target groups: classroom teachers, school administrators, local CES agents, and (for the pregnant teen material) a community health educator. The collective efforts of 41 CES staff, 100 teachers and school administrators, and 16 community health educators were reflected in the training teams.

Each regional training team was charged

with distributing the program to peer teachers and supporting its use through local or area workshops. Teams were encouraged to foster links between school-based personnel and local community resources in a way that would promote long-term involvement and continuity in nutrition education. The involvement of local CES agents made this possible.

The 15 training teams received initial training, support materials, ongoing technical assistance, and a small stipend from Cornell. NET educators provided extended distribution and maintenance of the program. The NET-CES partnership was a key to long-term programming.

Evaluation Methods and Results

Over 90 percent of the teachers who attended local workshops during the project's first year rated them as excellent or good. Teachers were excited about the new teaching materials and planned how to use them in their classrooms to meet curriculum goals. As one educator said, "It's a comprehensive approach and it ties in not only home, school, and community but also departments within the school."

Nutrition for Life makes teaching easier, better organized, more up-to-date, and more detailed, according to the majority of teachers questioned in a statewide random survey. Teachers also agree that students became more involved and interested in learning about nutrition.

Tools used to evaluate the effectiveness of Nutrition for Life included: (1) a mail survey of 2,425 randomly selected K-12 teachers in New York State and (2) a written nutrition test of 2,863 7th and 8th grade students from 103 randomly selected classrooms.

Results of these evaluations indicated that about half the 7th and 8th grade health and home and career skills teachers received the program, as did one-third of high school health, home economics, and physical education teachers, and one-fourth of elementary school teachers in New York State. Three-fourths of the teachers who received Nutrition for Life used the materials in teaching, and the teachers who attended training workshops were most likely to use the materials.

Modest but statistically significant effects on students' knowledge, attitudes, and behavior were found in classrooms where Nutrition for Life was used. In schools with a high proportion of low-income students, additional hours of Nutrition for Life teaching was associated with significantly higher nutrition attitude and behavior scores, compared with those of students in other schools.

Making a Difference in the Nation's Health

Effective partnerships among NET, CES, school administrators, teachers, and community health educators are needed to tackle complex and expansive issues such as health promotion. Nutrition for Life affords the opportunity for reaching the Nation's more than 41 million children and adolescents with effective school-based nutrition education.

USDA
Nutrition
Research

PART 2

Recent Advances in Maternal and Infant Nutrition

Nancy F. Butte
Associate Professor,
USDA-ARS Children's Nutrition
Research Center,
Department of Pediatrics,
Baylor College of Medicine,
Houston, TX

Milk fat provides infants with the essential fatty acids important for the growth of their neurological tissue and cell membranes. It also provides about 50 percent of their energy needs. Scientists need to understand how dietary fat is used to produce human milk, so food recommendations can be formulated for breastfeeding mothers.

Maternal Nutrition and Lactation

Most of the dietary fatty acids consumed by lactating women are (1) converted to energy through oxidation, (2) secreted into milk, or (3) stored in maternal adipose tissues. The Children's Nutrition Research Center has studied what happens to dietary fats in lactating, well-nourished women who consume either a low-fat diet or a high-fat diet. The diets were randomly assigned to 16 women who were nursing their infants. Figure 1 shows how dietary fat was used for energy, secreted into milk, or stored as fat.

The results of the study indicate that women on the low-fat diet had a lower concentration of fat in their milk but produced greater amounts of milk. Thus, their daily secretion of milk fat did not change, but their total carbohydrate production increased. The study also indicates that women with more body fat are better able to store dietary lipids and consequently may have difficulty losing weight.

In contrast, Otomi Indian women living in rural Mexico who consume a low-fat diet and have low body fat may produce milk that has a low fat content. Lactation was studied in these women because their infants were growing poorly. The Otomi women consume a low-fat, corn-predominant diet. Although their milk production rates were actually 15-20 percent higher than rates reported for well-nourished women, the concentrations of fat and energy in their milk were lower and may have contributed to the poor growth of their infants.

Infant Nutrition

Growth standards for infants from the National Center for Health Statistics (NCHS), Washington, DC, were derived primarily from

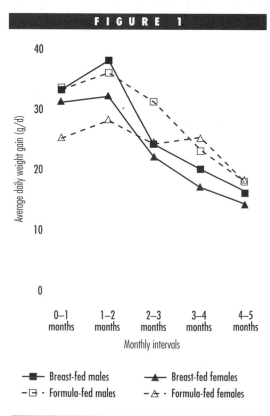

FIGURE 1

Composition of weight gain in breast-fed and formula-fed infants

- ■ - Breast-fed males
- □ - Formula-fed males
- ▲ - Breast-fed females
- △ - Formula-fed females

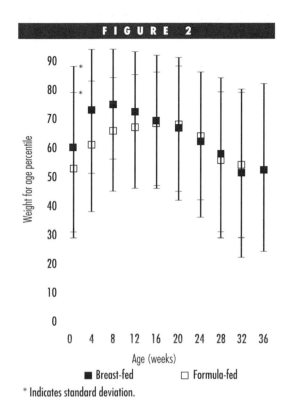

FIGURE 2

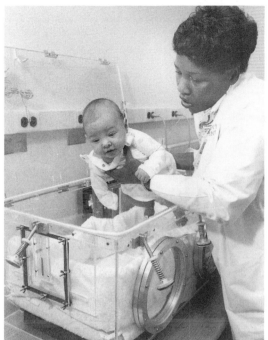

Adam Gillum, USDA/ARS Children's Nutrition Research Center

* Indicates standard deviation.

Photo:
Betty Walker, a research nurse, removes a baby from a calorimetry chamber after measuring the child's sleeping metabolic rate. This is part of the research testing at the Children's Nutrition Research Center.

Figure 2:
Growth of breast-fed and formula fed infants measured by growth standards of the National Center for Health Statistics (courtesy of I.F. Stuff)

formula-fed infants studied 20-50 years ago (fig. 2). Efforts are now under way to revise growth standards for infants. In a study at the Children's Nutrition Research Center, the growth of breast-fed and formula-fed infants was monitored for 9 months. Investigators found that formula-fed infants gained more weight after 3 months than breast-fed infants of the same age (fig. 3).

Until recently, most nutrition studies in infants relied on measurements of weight and length to estimate growth and body composi-tion. Today, however, scientists have new tech-niques, such as total body electrical conductivi-ty, to measure lean and fat body mass. Surprisingly, initial studies suggest that breast-fed infants may have more body fat than formu-la-fed infants. Other methods make it possible to measure how infants use the nutrients in the food they eat. Using indirect calorimetry and the doubly labeled water ($^2H_2{}^{18}O$) method, investigators have shown that breast-fed infants not only consume fewer calories than formula-fed babies but also expend fewer calories.

Besides differences in how breast-fed and formula-fed infants use calories, there are important differences in their biochemical

Percentages of dietary fat oxidized for energy, secreted into milk, and stored as fat in lactating women receiving high- and how-fat diets (courtesy of D.L. Hachey)

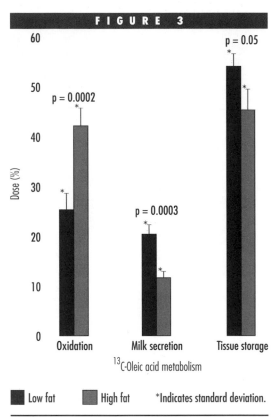

FIGURE 3

Dose (%)

p = 0.05

p = 0.0002

p = 0.0003

Oxidation   Milk secretion   Tissue storage

^{13}C-Oleic acid metabolism

■ Low fat   ■ High fat   *Indicates standard deviation.

makeup. Breast-fed infants have higher plasma cholesterol concentrations than formula-fed infants, presumably because of the higher cholesterol content of human milk than formula. The synthesis of cholesterol in breast-fed infants is one-third that of formula-fed infants. Scientists are now trying to determine how cholesterol intake in infancy affects cholesterol levels in adulthood.

Nutrition of the Preterm Infant

The survival rate of preterm infants has increased dramatically in the last several years; at least 90 percent of infants born prematurely survive. Scientists are studying differences in the composition of human and cow's milk to determine the levels of nutrients most suitable for preterm infants. Feeding human milk to preterm infants appears to be advantageous, because (1) the fat content of human milk is more appropriate than that of cow's milk for infant brain development, and (2) the levels of immunoglobulins in human milk may increase an infant's ability to defend against infection. Human milk, however, is "designed" by nature for full-term infants, whose bones are more fully developed, so investigators at the Children's Nutrition Research Center are studying how much additional calcium and phosphorus must be added to human milk to ensure healthy bone growth in preterm infants.

Studying Postnatal Growth and Development

Some infant nutrition questions must be studied in animals, such as the infant pig, to avoid the possibility of harming human subjects. Scientists at the Children's Nutrition Research Center are studying genetically lean and obese piglets to learn how fat and cholesterol are used in early life. They have found that cholesterol levels in genetically obese piglets continue to rise when their diets contain cholesterol, suggesting that these piglets may not be able to shut down cholesterol synthesis when cholesterol is provided in the diet. Studies have also shown that piglets with low levels of plasma cholesterol grow more slowly than piglets with higher levels. Because infant

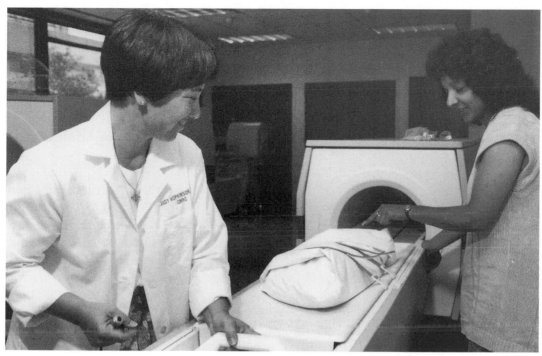

Judy Hopkinson of the Children's Nutrition Research Center prepares to use a total body electrical conductivity machine during nutritional research testing as the infant's mother looks on.

Adam Gillum, USDA/ARS Children's Nutrition Research Center

formula has very little cholesterol compared with human milk, both findings are important in designing human infant formulas, whether for full-term or preterm infants.

Rats are also studied to learn more about human infants. Because they are particularly immature at birth, rats are relevant to studies of preterm infants. Investigators have found that before 10 days of age, the weight gain of rat pups consists almost entirely of protein, with very little increase in body fat. This phenomenon can also be seen in preterm infants. From the studies in rats, scientists have learned that adequate nutrition immediately after birth is very important to ensure normal maturation.

Continuing Research

Nutrient utilization in lactating females and their offspring is being investigated through noninvasive techniques and animal models. We have yet to fully understand how maternal diet and nutritional status affect milk composition and how dietary manipulation of infant weight gain, body composition, and serum cholesterol affects health later in life. Studies to ensure that preterm infants get adequate nutrition will enable normal growth and development and promote optimal cognitive and immune functions. Both short- and long-term effects of infant nutrition on the developing organism are important in defining the nutritional requirements of infants.

Recent Advances in Nutrition: From Adolescence to Adulthood

William W. Wong
Associate Professor,
USDA-ARS Children's Nutrition
Research Center,
Department of Pediatrics,
Baylor College of Medicine,
Houston, TX

Diet recommendations for adolescents cannot be improved until scientists have more information about nutrient intakes, body compositions, and energy expenditures for adolescents.

Basic Nutritional Requirements of Adolescents

Most recommendations have relied on body measurements to index growth. To date, nutrient requirements for growth during adolescence have been estimated from studies of fetuses or adults. Because tissue composition during growth differs among different age groups, it is not appropriate to measure growth in teenagers using techniques that were developed to measure growth in adults and fetuses. In addition, most studies have been done on Caucasians; very few have been conducted on individuals of other ethnic groups. Data in the literature suggest that there are differences among ethnic groups in growth rate, metabolic rate, body composition, and onset of fertility.

To assess the nutritional needs of teenagers (including obese or pregnant teens), scientists must collect data on nutrient intakes, body composition, and energy expenditure from healthy adolescents who represent different ethnic groups.

Adolescence is the transition period between childhood and adulthood. The growth spurt that occurs during adolescence includes rapid bone growth, increased muscle mass, and increased body fat. The growth and development of adolescents reflect their genetic background and

their dietary history during infancy and childhood. The food choices made by adolescents affect not only their growth and development during puberty but also their reproductive capacity and susceptibility to degenerative diseases when they become adults.

Nutritional Problems of Adolescents

Obesity

Because of the high fat content of the American diet, obesity affects 10 to 35 percent of adolescents. Researchers have shown that infant weight correlates strongly with adult weight and that children who are overweight before puberty have a 75 percent chance of becoming obese adults. It has also been shown that those who are overweight after puberty have a 95 percent chance of becoming obese adults. It is not surprising, therefore, that data from the Second National Health and Nutrition Examination Survey (1976-80) indicated that approximately 34 million American adults (25.7 percent) are overweight.

Although fat deposition during puberty is essential for teenage girls in preparation for reproduction and lactation, the incidence of obesity in the United States is unfortunately high, especially in adult women. Obesity is associated with increased risk of diabetes, high blood pressure, heart disease, gallbladder disease, colon cancer, postmenopausal breast cancer, and menstrual irregularities. Unless obese women eat a prudent diet during pregnancy, they have a great risk of complications.

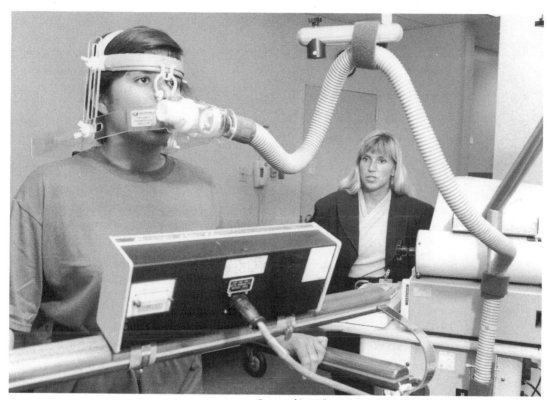

Photo 1.
Cardiorespiratory fitness of a 15-year-old is evaluated under the supervision of exercise physiologist Molly Bray.

Courtesy of Dr. William Wong, USDA/ARS Children's Nutrition Research Center

Pregnancy and Osteoporosis

The National Center for Health Statistics recently documented the sharpest rise in teenage pregnancies in 15 years; the annual incidence in the United States is now 1 in 10. The effects of pregnancy during adolescence on long-term health status are not completely understood. A female adolescent generally attains 99 percent of her mother's bone size and 80 to 95 percent of her mother's bone mass and bone density by 14 years of age. The growth spurt and onset of fertility that occur during puberty impose substantial nutrient demands on female adolescents.

The consequences of these changes during puberty depend on individual nutritional status, level of sexual maturity, and genetic background. An increasing health problem in the United States is posed by pregnant and lactating teenaged girls, who must accommodate the additional nutrient demands of reproduction. These girls are at high risk of nutrient deficiencies, such as calcium deficiency, and thus have a higher risk of devel-

47

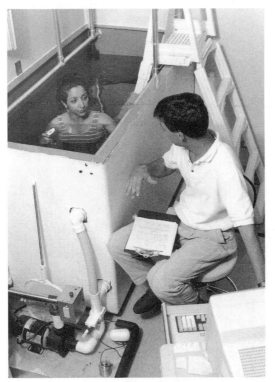

Courtesy of Dr. William Wong,
USDA/ARS Children's Nutrition Research Center

oping osteoporosis later in life. There are many nutrition questions to be answered about pregnancy during adolescence.

Cholesterol and Atherosclerosis

Cholesterol is an essential component of cell membranes and is required for cell growth, replication, and maintenance. Plasma cholesterol concentrations are known to be higher in breast-fed infants than in formula-fed infants, perhaps because human milk has a higher cholesterol content than formula. Although cholesterol causes atherosclerosis

in humans, animal studies have shown that a diet high in cholesterol early in life may protect against diets high in cholesterol later in life. The protective mechanism, however, has not been documented in humans.

Nutrition Research at the Children's Nutrition Research Center

The Children's Nutrition Research Center (CNRC) has developed numerous noninvasive techniques to measure lean body mass, fat mass, bone mineral content and density, basal metabolic rate, and total energy expenditure. Several studies are in progress at the CNRC to assess the nutrient requirements of adolescents.

In one cross-sectional study, nutrient intakes, cardiorespiratory fitness, body composition, energy expenditure, plasma lipid profile, and plasma iron status are being measured in 200 healthy female adolescents between 10 and 16 years of age. Equal numbers of adolescents representing four ethnic groups (white, black, Hispanic, and Asian) are being studied. Nutrient intakes for a 3-day period are being analyzed from food records. Cardiorespiratory fitness is being evaluated by determining the maximal heart rate and maximum oxygen utilization while the subject is walking and running on a motorized treadmill (see photo 1). Body density is being measured by weighing the subject in and out of the water (see photo 2). Because fat is less dense than water, lower body density reflects higher body fat. Lean body mass is being estimated in a total body electrical conductivity

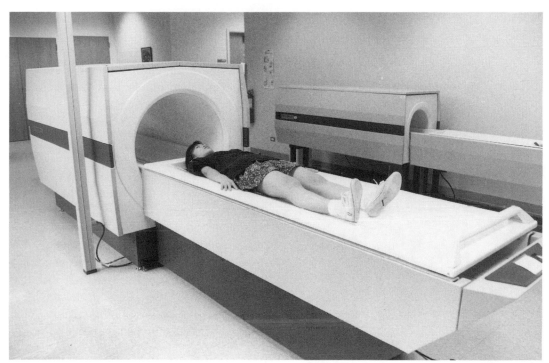

Photo 3.
Lean body mass and body fat of a 14-year-old are measured by a total body electrical conductivity (TOBEC) machine.

Dr. William Wong, USDA/ARS Children's Nutrition Research Center

(TOBEC) machine (see photo 3). The TOBEC machine has been approved for use on infants, children, and adults by the Food and Drug Administration. Total body bone mineral content and density are being measured by a technique called dual-energy x-ray absorptiometry (see photo 4). The subject lies in a supine position during the whole-body scan, which takes approximately 15 minutes.

The energy required for daily activities, including sleep, is being measured while the subject is inside a whole-body indirect calorimeter for 24 hours. The whole-body calorimeter is similar in size to a small bed-room (see photo 5) and has a bed, table, chair, television, VCR, stereo system, exercise bicycle, telephone, and toilet facilities. The subject also eats breakfast, lunch, and dinner in the calorimeter. The 24-hour energy expenditure measured reflects the caloric needs of the subject while being confined in the chamber. Activities inside the calorimeter, however, are limited. Because the subject is being monitored constantly inside the chamber, behavior and activity patterns are not typical. The whole-body calorimeter provides important information on basic energy needs but does not provide an accurate esti-

Photo 4.
Dr. William Wong uses a dual energy x-ray absorptiometer to measure the bone mineral content and bone density of a 14-year-old.

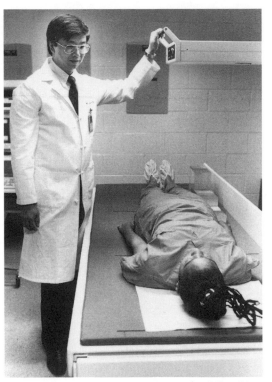

Courtesy of Dr. William Wong,
USDA/ARS Children's Nutrition Research Center

sample is tested for plasma total cholesterol, triglyceride, high-density and low-density lipoprotein cholesterol, apolipoproteins A-1 and B, total iron, and ferritin. The relationships of nutrient intake, body composition, caloric needs, cardiorespiratory fitness, plasma lipid profile, and iron status to each other and to sexual maturity and race are being evaluated.

Another study underway at the CNRC will establish a body composition database for both men and women. Results from this study will define the relationships between nutrient intake and body composition of healthy children from infancy through adolescence for different ethnic groups. The data will also establish acceptable upper and lower limits within which to evaluate children who are ill. Approximately 1,000 healthy children under 18 years of age from 3 ethnic groups (white, black, and Hispanic) are being studied in the Metabolic Research Unit and Body Composition Laboratory at the CNRC.

Two studies at CNRC are designed to define the nutrient needs of pregnant and lactating teenagers. One longitudinal study will estimate the nutrient intakes, changes in body composition, and changes in energy expenditure of 20 healthy pregnant teenagers under 17 years of age. These teenagers are being studied four times between 8 and 40 weeks of gestation and immediately after delivery. The other study will measure the dietary intakes, milk production, and changes in body composition and growth in lactating adolescents. Preliminary results indicate that

mate of the caloric needs of the subject in a free-living environment.

The energy needs of free-living subjects are being estimated using the doubly labeled water method. After a baseline saliva sample is collected, each subject drinks a known amount of water containing the stable isotopes deuterium and oxygen-18. The energy expenditures of the free-living subjects are calculated from the rates of disappearance of these isotopes in subsequent saliva samples. A blood sample is collected from each subject after the subjects have fasted overnight. Each

body weight, lean body mass, and body fat in lactating adolescents are maintained during the first 3 months after giving birth. This conservation of body mass may occur at the expense of milk production in the adolescent mother.

To test the hypothesis that early neonatal ingestion of large quantities of cholesterol protects the infant from high-cholesterol diets later in life, the CNRC is planning to study the effects of dietary cholesterol on in vivo cholesterol synthesis. The studies will be conducted in 4-month-old infants: 12 exclusively breast-fed, 12 formula-fed, and 12 formula-fed with added cholesterol. Later, all infants will be fed a formula with low cholesterol levels. The same procedure will be repeated at 11 months of age. The infants will then be fed a diet high in cholesterol, and the effects of the diet on the cholesterol levels in the infants will be evaluated.

The United States is confronted with phenomenal economic costs from obesity, adolescent pregnancy, poor birth outcomes, and cardiovascular heart diseases related to atherosclerosis. The data collected in the CNRC studies will provide important information for the formulation of food recommendations for healthy teenagers as well as obese and pregnant teenagers. We hope these recommendations, besides helping to provide adequate education, will also help reduce nutrition-related health costs in our society.

Photo 5.
A 14-year-old exercises on an ergometer in a whole-body calorimeter at the Children's Nutrition Research Center.

Courtesy of Dr. William Wong,
USDA/ARS Children's Nutrition Research Center

Nutrition and Cardiovascular Fitness

F. W. Thye
Associate Professor of
Human Nutrition and Foods,
College of Human Resources,
Virginia Polytechnic
Institute and State University,
Blacksburg, VA

Although the number of deaths from heart disease has been steadily declining since the 1960's, heart disease remains the number one killer in the United States. Moreover, all vascular diseases, including heart disease, stroke, and other blood-vessel diseases, accounted for almost half of all deaths in 1988.

Hypercholesterolemia (high cholesterol), high blood pressure, and smoking are still considered the most important risk factors associated with heart disease. Recently identified as risk factors are obesity, a sedentary lifestyle, and high-density lipoprotein (HDL) cholesterol concentrations of less than 35 milligrams per deciliter (mg/dL). Although weight loss and exercise are independent risk factors for heart disease, they are both recommended for raising HDL-cholesterol levels, decreasing plasma total cholesterol and triglycerides, improving glucose tolerance, and lowering high blood pressure.

Guidelines for Plasma Cholesterol

Plasma total cholesterol is now commonly used as a screening tool to identify persons who are at high risk (greater than 240 mg/dL) of developing heart disease. Although there is no question that plasma total cholesterol is associated with increased risk of heart disease, the use of plasma total cholesterol as an indicator to predict the risk of heart disease on an individual basis is relatively weak, whereas low-density lipoprotein (LDL)- and HDL-cholesterol concentrations have a much stronger predictive value. High levels of LDL-cholesterol (greater than 160 mg/dL) and very low concentrations of HDL-cholesterol (less than 35 mg/dL) are strongly correlated with increased incidence of heart disease. We need to know the LDL- and HDL-cholesterol concentrations before we can accurately predict the risk of heart disease for each person.

Recent studies showed that fully 20 percent of the population thought to have desirable levels of plasma total cholesterol (less than 200 mg/dL) and low risk of heart disease actually had levels of HDL-cholesterol that were too low (less than 35 mg/dL). With one other risk factor, such as being male, these persons would instead be classified at high risk of heart disease. Several studies have shown that the risk of developing heart disease, as determined by LDL-cholesterol concentrations, was markedly decreased as HDL-cholesterol concentrations increased.

Plasma total cholesterol is a practical and relatively inexpensive method for identifying individuals at high risk of heart disease on a population-wide basis. The results of the Lipid Research Clinic-Coronary Primary Prevention Trial, which studied 3,800 men for 7 years and was coordinated by the Centers for Disease Control, confirmed the results of other epidemiological and clinical studies: that lowering the plasma total cholesterol lowers the risk of heart disease. Lowering plasma total cholesterol by 1 percent reduced the risk of heart disease deaths and other heart disease end points by 2 percent in individuals who were hypercholesterolemic.

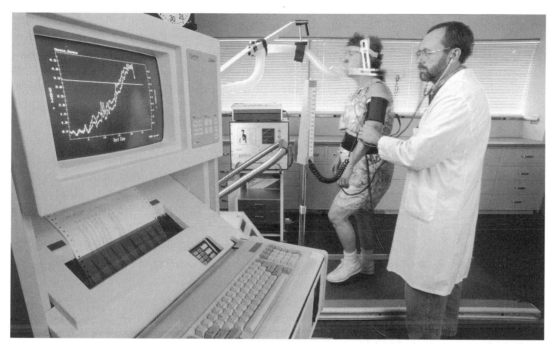

Physiologist Henry Lukaski calculates a volunteer's oxygen intake and carbon dioxide output.

Bruce Fritz/USDA 92BW1234-21

Modification of Diet

A strong body of evidence from various studies on dietary modification, purified diet, and epidemiology indicates that plasma total cholesterol and LDL-cholesterol levels can be markedly decreased in most individuals and consistently across the population by lowering total fat and especially the saturated fatty acids in the diet. It is thought that saturated fatty acids interfere with LDL removal from the blood (by reducing the number of LDL receptors to catabolize LDL), resulting in increased concentrations of plasma LDL-cholesterol.

Present dietary guidelines recommend the consumption of less than 30 percent of calories from fat, with less than 10 percent of calories coming from saturated fatty acids. Research over many years has shown that increasing the levels of polyunsaturated fatty acids (PUFA) and of monounsaturated fatty acids (MUFA) in the diet is also an effective way of lowering plasma total cholesterol and LDL-cholesterol. Unfortunately, PUFA also lower plasma HDL-cholesterol; fortunately, MUFA do not.

There is more to be learned about the effect of the individual fatty acids in the diet, because it appears that not all saturated fatty acids raise plasma cholesterol. Recent work with stearic acid (18-carbon, saturated) shows that it does not raise plasma total cholesterol and in fact may lower it, whereas two other saturated fatty acids, palmitic (16-carbon) or myristic (14-carbon) acids, raise plasma total cholesterol and LDL-cholesterol when fed as the predominant fatty acid. Future recommendations for restricting or including certain foods in the diet should take this information into consideration.

Epidemiological studies have indicated a decreased incidence of heart disease in certain populations that regularly consume fish. However, work with fish oils that contain n-3 fatty acids has found a consistent reduction only in plasma triglycerides and relatively little effect on the plasma cholesterol levels. This indicates the need for more information before any recommendations can be made about the inclusion of fish-oil fatty acids in the diet.

The present consumption of cholesterol averages about 300 mg/day, with women consuming less than that and men consuming more. Most persons do not respond to changes in dietary cholesterol with increased or decreased plasma levels of cholesterol over a wide range of cholesterol intakes. Only one-third of the population is sensitive to dietary cholesterol and would probably benefit from further reductions in the present dietary guideline of no more than 300 mg cholesterol per day.

Fiber and Cholesterol

Increased levels of dietary fiber are effective in lowering plasma total cholesterol and LDL-cholesterol. With the emphasis on more fruit, vegetables, and grain products, low-fat diets (less than 30 percent of calories from fat) are generally higher in dietary fiber. Although the results are not as consistent or as dramatic as those from low-saturated-fatty-acid diets, the higher levels of soluble dietary fiber from oat products and legumes have been shown to lower plasma total cholesterol and LDL-cholesterol concentrations. This was found in a wide assortment of studies with different levels and sources of dietary fiber.

Preliminary evidence shows that, as in some animal species, reversal of the atherosclerotic buildup (of cholesterol and other material) in the coronary vessels can occur in humans. Although several types of lifestyle changes occurred at the same time (including exercise and meditation), the dietary hallmark of this research was a very-low-fat diet (about 10 percent of calories from fat) with emphasis on fruits, vegetables, and cereals. It is not known whether this will result in recommendations to reduce fat consumption still further; substantiating research is required.

Weight Reduction

Fully one-quarter of the malc population and almost half of all women in the United States are trying to lose weight. From 30 to 40 million American adults (between 20 and 74 years old) are overweight, and over 12 million are obese. Those conditions are associated with low HDL-cholesterol levels, decreased glucose tolerance, high blood pressure, and elevated plasma cholesterol and triglycerides. Since obesity is an independent risk factor for heart disease, and since it is also a risk factor in association with several others, decreasing the incidence of obesity and overweight may be the single most important intervention for cardiovascular health. Evidence continues to accumulate on the position that weight loss and exercise will increase plasma HDL-cholesterol. At present, losing weight and exercising are the only recommendations that can be made by professionals to raise HDL levels. In addition, both are important remedies for lowering blood pressure, improving glucose tolerance, and decreasing plasma total triglycerides and cholesterol.

Exercise is an excellent adjunct to weight loss because exercise burns calories and promotes fatty acid release from the fat tissue. It has been shown that exercise is a valuable tool in the maintenance of weight loss, which is now considered by health professionals to be as important as the initial weight loss. In addition, recently published articles indicate that low-fat (20 percent of calories or less) diets were effective in weight reduction and in maintenance of weight loss. It therefore seems reasonable that exercise and lower fat diets should be used together to effectively reduce a number of risk factors and thereby enhance cardiovascular health.

Education

Low-fat diets and increased activity seem to be a relatively simple, straightforward message for the average consumer. However, many consumers are simply unaware of the differences in caloric contents of fat, carbohydrate, and protein. In fact, many persons still cut high-carbohydrate foods such as bread and potatoes from the diet when "watching their calories."

Although some people may recognize that oils and visible fat on meats are more calorie dense than potatoes and bread, they are unaware that fried potatoes, fried meats, many processed meats (such as wieners and luncheon meats), and some baked goods (such as muffins, biscuits, and pastries) are very high in so-called hidden-fat calories.

The frozen convenience items for the microwave oven are a new generation of products that are often consumed without a thought as to how much fat is in them. The place of fast food in the eating pattern of the average American has been firmly established. Although some in the fast-food industry have attempted to provide low-fat items, the overwhelming number of high-fat selections makes it difficult for even the most knowledgeable consumers to select a low-fat balanced meal.

A more aggressive program of nutrition education for employees in the Nation's school cafeterias is needed to meet the recently adopted dietary guidelines of less than 30 percent of calories from fat and less than 10 percent of calories from saturated fat. And finally, hints for low-fat cooking need to be more widely and effectively disseminated to the American public. All these limitations of knowledge, motivation, or skills present a significant challenge to the nutrition or health educator.

Maintaining a Strong Skeleton

Connie M. Weaver
Head, Department of
Foods and Nutrition,
Purdue University,
West Lafayette, IN

Approximately 95 percent of our skeleton is developed during the first 18 years of life. Periods of rapid growth occur during the first year of life and during the adolescent growth spurt. After adult height is achieved, our bones continue to become more dense as minerals are deposited. This is the consolidation phase. An additional 5-percent increase in bone mass is accumulated by age 30 to 35. At this age, our bones are the most dense and we are in a period of peak bone mass. After age 40, we experience an age-related phase of slow bone loss. The most rapid loss of bone mass for women occurs during the first 4 to 8 years after menopause. This chapter discusses the consequences of bone loss and also the lifestyle factors that protect the skeleton.

Osteoporosis

When enough bone mass is lost that bones become vulnerable to fracture, the individual has developed osteoporosis. Osteoporosis is a debilitating disease that affects over 24 million Americans. Each year in the United States, 1.3 million fractures are attributable to osteoporosis. The most common fractures occur at the wrist, the spine, and the hip. Hip fractures alone result in annual health-care costs of $10 billion. This figure will continue to increase with the increase of the elderly population. Between 15 and 25 percent of persons with a hip fracture enter long-term-care institutions. Hip fractures are associated with a high mortality rate due to surgical deaths and to complications such as thromboembolism, fat embolism, and pneumonia.

Treatment of Osteoporosis

A number of drugs are being investigated for their efficacy in the treatment of osteoporosis. These include calcitonin, bisphosphonates, and 1,25-dihydroxyvitamin D3. These drugs slow bone resorption but have little effect on the stimulation of bone formation. Other agents being researched are fluoride and parathyroid hormone; these may stimulate bone formation but are not proven to reduce the rates of fracture.

Because of the lack of a cure for osteoporosis, the prevention of excessive bone loss is the current focus. Approximately 80 percent of bone mass is genetically determined. The other 20 percent can be modified by lifestyle factors. Adequate calcium intake, weight-bearing exercise, and estrogen-replacement therapy for women who have entered menopause are the primary lifestyle factors associated with reducing the risk of osteoporosis. Factors associated with increased risk of osteoporosis include smoking and abuse of alcohol and caffeine. Thin, small-framed women are more vulnerable to osteoporosis, and Caucasians and Asians are at higher risk than African-Americans. Women are at greater risk than men by a ratio of 4 to 1. Women have less bone mass, experience accelerated loss of bone mass following menopause, and ingest less calcium than do men.

A researcher at the USDA Human Nutrition Research Center at Tufts University (Boston, MA), Bess Dawson-Hughes, has shown that calcium supplements can prevent the usual bone loss associated with aging in

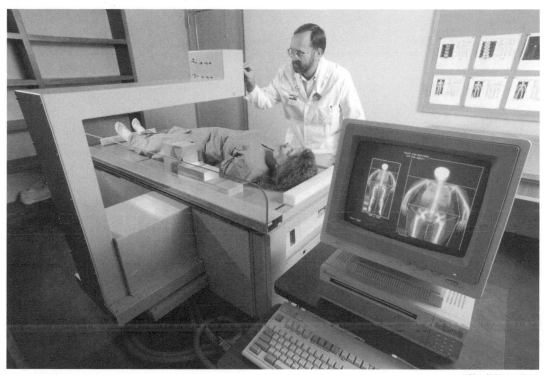

USDA/92BW1234-2

Building bone mass in early life may be the most effective way to prevent osteoporosis in later life.

women who consume less than 400 milligrams (mg) of calcium per day. Furthermore, two studies have reported that the risk of hip fracture is reduced by as much as 60 percent on higher calcium intakes.

Other nutrients that are important to the skeleton are protein, vitamins C and D, phosphorus, magnesium, manganese, copper, zinc, and boron.

Estrogen-replacement therapy can also prevent or retard bone loss in perimenopausal and postmenopausal women as long as the therapy is continued and the dietary calcium intake is sufficient. Calcium supplementation in combi-nation with estrogen replacement has syner-gistic positive effects on bone loss; that is, the effectiveness of each treatment is enhanced.

Early-Life Steps To Prevent Osteoporosis

Building bone mass in early life may be the most effective way to prevent osteoporosis in later life. If this opportunity is missed, it prob-ably cannot be made up. Even small increases in bone mass can have a great impact on the risk of fracture. For instance, a 5-percent increase in bone mass can reduce the risk of osteoporotic fracture by 40 percent.

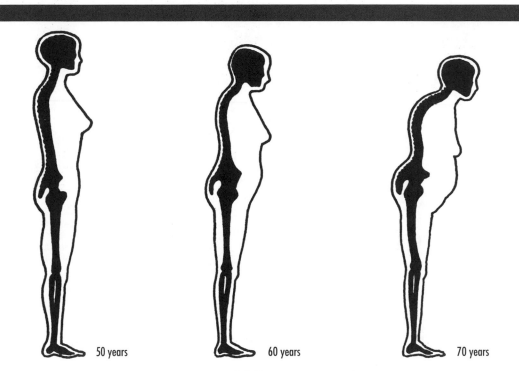

50 years   60 years   70 years

Progressive spinal deformity in osteoporosis

A lifelong habit of drinking milk is associated with increased bone mass. Researchers at the Indiana University School of Medicine in Indianapolis have shown that calcium supplements increase the bone mass in preadolescent children, compared to that in their identical twins who received placebos during a 3-year study.

Getting Enough Calcium
In the American diet, almost 75 percent of dietary calcium comes from dairy products. Few other foods are concentrated sources of absorbable calcium. At Purdue University (West Lafayette, IN) and Creighton University (Omaha, NE), plant foods are being screened for calcium absorption. These include broccoli, bok choy, kale, and tofu made with calcium salts. Calcium is well absorbed from these vegetables and from all dairy products—that

is, milk, yogurt, cheese, processed cheese, and their low-fat counterparts. Spinach is a concentrated source of calcium, but this calcium is poorly absorbed because it is complexed with oxalic acid and is therefore indigestible.

Depending on their stage of growth, people need 2 to 5 cups of milk or the calcium equivalent each day. American females more than 12 years old typically consume less calcium than this recommended amount. Calcium intake in American women is 40 to 50 percent below that in men. A 1984 National Institutes of Health consensus-development conference recommended 1,000 mg of calcium per day for premenopausal women and 1,500 mg per day for postmenopausal women. However, 25 percent of American women have an intake below 300 mg per day, which is the amount of calcium in one glass of milk. Calcium supplements are recommended for individuals who cannot get adequate calcium through diet. However, supplements do not contain all the nutrients necessary for building bones, and people often forget to take pills. An alternative source of calcium is the fortified beverages now on the market.

Exercise

Weight-bearing exercise has a positive impact on bone density. An effective exercise program applies weight loading to all parts of the skeleton. For example, the right arm of a right-handed tennis player has a higher bone density than does the left arm. Activities that are exclusively aerobic seem to be the least effective in building peak bone mass. Thus, weight lifters have higher bone density than do swimmers. We do not know if the positive effects of exercise on bone mass are retained when exercise is discontinued.

A partial explanation for bone loss in the elderly is the reduction in physical activity with age. The physical work of the average sedentary elderly adult is 30 percent less than that of the average younger adult. If immobilization occurs, bone loss is accelerated; but bone mass can increase when the individual again becomes ambulatory.

The Known and Unknown

Obtaining adequate dietary calcium, exercise, and estrogen-replacement therapy following menopause are three lifestyle choices for maintaining a strong skeleton. The interaction of these factors is not well understood. Nor do we know the residual positive effect after cessation of treatment. Research to determine the best food sources of absorbable calcium and the most effective exercise programs, in combination with education programs on behavior modification, can help reduce the suffering and the health-care costs associated with bone loss.

Nutrition and a Robust Immune System

Tim R. Kramer
Research Biologist,
Beltsville Human Nutrition
Research Center, ARS, USDA
Beltsville, MD

Introduction

Nature has provided scientists with early opportunities to learn about the effect of nutrition on the immune system. Low-nutrient soils have caused mineral deficiencies in some populations of livestock and humans. By studying these populations, scientists discovered the importance of selenium to the immune system. Famines, natural disasters, severe poverty, and wartime have likewise provided us with many of our early learning opportunities about the relationships among nutrition, immune functions, and health. Many essential micronutrients (vitamins and minerals), such as copper and zinc, were once believed to be unessential to the human diet but are now known to be important for normal immune function.

Thorough examination of the effects of nutrient deficiencies, combined with clinical observations and detailed investigations, is helping us understand the relationship between nutrition and immune function. This chapter briefly highlights the effects of nutrient deficiencies and overnutrition on a competent immune system and mentions some current research.

Nutrient Deficiencies

Generalized malnutrition, historically referred to as protein-energy malnutrition (PEM), often coexists with deficiencies of one

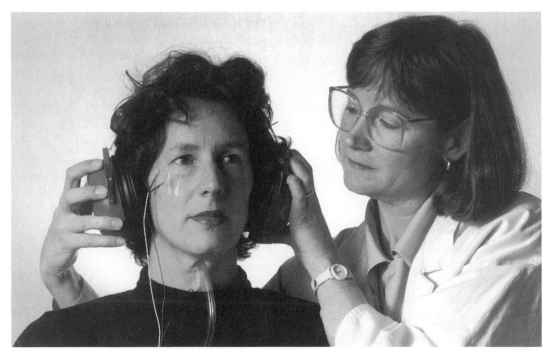

A research nutrition scientist, Monica Schaeffer (right) prepares ARS physiologist Teresa Barbieri for a startle test that measures the central nervous system's reactivity.

Perry Rech/USDA 90BW279-4

or more micronutrients. PEM is one of the earliest forms of malnutrition to have attracted the interest of the medical community. The association between severe PEM and atrophy of the thymus gland (primary lymphoid tissue) was described nearly 150 years ago, even before it was realized that the thymus is a principal body organ of the immune system. Beginning as early as 1911, several investigators documented that thymic atrophy results from malnutrition due to food scarcity or from illness associated with cachexia (severe weight loss due to diseases such as cancer). Malnutrition also commonly causes atrophy of the tonsils (secondary lymphoid tissue).

During the first half of this century, an association between severe PEM and increased infections was described. But it was not until the 1960's, when the important role of the thymus as a primary source of cells (T-lymphocytes) of the immune system became known, that the relationships among nutrition, immunity, and health were established. During the past 20 years, it has become clear that PEM in children and adults reduces the number and function of T-helper immune lymphocytes, which promote an active immune-protective response against infectious and other diseases, such as cancer.

Healthy subjects who are fed balanced meals, but in restricted amounts, show suppressed immunity similar to that of children and hospital patients with PEM. ARS and U.S. Army researchers have found that young, healthy men consuming less energy in the

In a test to determine effects of vitamin levels on eyesight, a volunteer is asked to quickly sort poker chips in dim light.

Perry Rech/USDA 0278-19

form of food and drink than is required during heavy work and exercise show decreased immune function. In contrast to unhealthy subjects, such individuals show rapid correction of their immune functions when they receive enough calories to balance their energy demands.

The role of micronutrients in the immune system has been studied in individuals suffering from micronutrient deficiencies, such as hospitalized patients receiving liquid diets that lacked an unknown essential micronutrient, children living in regions deficient in select micronutrients, livestock grazing on mineral-deficient grassland, and research animals. Through such studies, the essential role of several minerals (iron, zinc, copper, magnesium, and selenium) and several vitamins (vitamin A, vitamin C, B-group vitamins, and vitamin E) has been demonstrated for normal immune functions. The mechanisms of their functions on the immune system and the safe range of intake are not fully under-

Judy Hopkinson prepares mother's milk for storage in the ARS Children's Nutrition Research Center milk bank for later research.

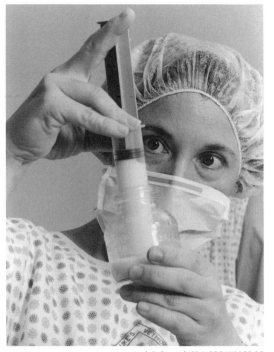

Jack Dykinga/USDA 0986X1108-19

stood. As with many nutrients, micronutrients interact with each other in maximizing their role in immune function.

High-Fat Diets

Consuming too much fat can have a suppressive effect on the immune system. The lifestyle of many people of the industrialized world leads to diets that are high in fat.

From animal and human studies, it is known that both the concentration and type of dietary fats play a crucial role in the function of the immune system. Diets high in fat cause reduced resistance to infectious diseases in animals and suppressed cellular immune function in both animals and humans. At high concentration, polyunsaturated fats that are low in vitamin E appear to be more immunosuppressive than saturated fats.

The immunosuppressive effects of high-fat diets can be lessened by eating foods containing antioxidants (certain vitamins and minerals) that neutralize these effects. Foods that have a stabilizing effect on the immune system include those containing vitamin E (oils, shortening, margarine, fruits, and green leafy vegetables), vitamin C (fruits and vegetables), beta-carotene (brightly colored fruits and vegetables), selenium (meats, cereals, dairy products, fruits, and vegetables), copper (liver, nuts, and whole-grain cereals) and manganese (nuts, whole-grain cereals, dried legumes, and tea).

Current and Needed Work

Early studies on nutrition and the immune system involved severe nutritional deficiencies. Since more sophisticated laboratory techniques are now available, ARS researchers are now able to compile information to establish the effects of moderate nutritional alteration on the immune system. Although our understanding of the role of nutrition in the immune system is increasing, considerably more work is needed before we can use the information to improve health.

Work describing maturation of the immune system in breast-fed and bottle-fed infants is needed. Most milk formulas for infants in the Western World are now considered to meet the conventional nutritional requirements of newborn infants. Despite this, investigation of the effects of breast- and bottle-feeding on select immune functions has shown that breast-feeding has contrasting effects on the development of immunity. In the early neonatal period, up to 6 weeks of age, there are enhanced immune responses in the breast-fed infants. But by 3 months of age, many of the immune responses are higher in formula-fed infants. These results suggest that, during the first 6 weeks, breast-fed infants are receiving enhanced immune protection from breast milk, while formula-fed infants must produce this immunity themselves. Developing immunity is not usually a problem for formula-fed infants in societies where the public health standards are high.

Many studies have documented the frequent occurrence of nutritional deficiencies in the elderly. Observations show that these deficiencies are associated with undernutrition due to reduced calorie intake; overall reduced intake; and lower blood levels of iron, zinc, vitamin C, B vitamins, and vitamin E. Socioeconomic deprivation, physical disability, isolation, dental problems, and increased nutrient needs due to underlying disease are common causes of nutritional problems in the elderly. Although it is logical to try to correct nutritional deficiencies in the elderly in order to improve their immune responses and reduce the risk of infectious disease and other age-related disorders, the desirability of taking megadose supplements of vitamins and minerals is questionable.

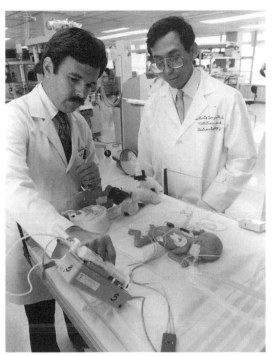

Richard Schanler (left) and Cutberto Garza monitor the feeding of a 7-week-old premature infant in the intensive care unit of Texas Children's Hospital in Houston.

Jack Dykinga/USDA 0986X1108-19

During the 150 years since a relationship between severe undernutrition and atrophy of the thymus gland was first described, our understanding of the role of nutrients on the immune system has increased tremendously. ARS researchers are now reaching the point where more can be learned about the effects of marginal changes in nutrition on immune protection against diseases. During this time, it is comforting to know that the body has tremendous capabilities for efficiently using nutrients, even in unbalanced amounts, and maximizing responsiveness of the immune system.

Energy Metabolism

Joan M. Conway
Research Chemist,
Energy and Protein
Nutrition Laboratory,
Beltsville Human Nutrition
Research Center,
Agricultural Research
Service, USDA,
Beltsville, MD

What Is Energy Metabolism?

Energy can be defined as the capacity for doing work. Metabolism is the sum of processes by which the body handles a particular substance. When scientists study energy metabolism, therefore, they are studying the processes that handle energy in the body.

What Is a Calorie?

The energy value of foods or beverages is expressed in terms of the kilocalorie. If a food is burned and the heat produced is measured, the quantity of heat produced expressed in kilocalories represents the gross energy value of the food. The gross energy value of food does not represent the energy available to the body (fig. 1). No food is completely utilized, since some of the energy is excreted in urine and feces. When corrections are made to account for this loss of excreted energy, the corrected energy value of foods is designated "metabolizable" energy. Energy values listed in food tables represent metabolizable energy. Although it is common to call the energy value of food "calories," it is more accurate to use the term "kilocalories."

Is a Calorie Really a Calorie?

The energy content of foods varies depending primarily on the amount of protein, fat, and carbohydrate contained in the specific food. The amounts of metabolizable energy in a gram of protein, fat, and carbohydrate are 4.0, 9.0, and 4.0 kilocalories, respectively. Although these nutrients are metabolized differently within the body, a kilocalorie from carbohydrate is the same as a kilocalorie from fat or protein.

What Is Energy Balance, or How Can I Maintain a Stable Body Weight?

Fig. 1 is a schematic diagram detailing energy balance in humans. After adjusting energy intake (from food and beverages) for energy excreted in human wastes, one can determine the calories absorbed by the body—or metabolizable energy. In order for a person to maintain a stable body weight, metabolizable energy must be equally balanced with energy expenditure—that is, the calories expended to perform physical and metabolic work.

When metabolizable energy is greater than energy expenditure, the excess energy is stored in the body as protein, carbohydrate, or largely as fat. If energy expenditure is greater than metabolizable energy, then energy is mobilized from body energy stores. In fact, this storage and mobilization of energy is an ongoing cycle. During the day we store energy as either glycogen or fat; during sleep we mobilize energy to meet the metabolic work needs of the body. When a person is in energy balance, this daily rhythm is such that weight varies by only 2-3 pounds around a particular weight. However, when a person is in positive energy balance, then energy is being stored and weight increases. In order to lose weight, therefore, it is necessary to decrease energy intake below energy expenditure or to increase energy expenditure beyond energy intake.

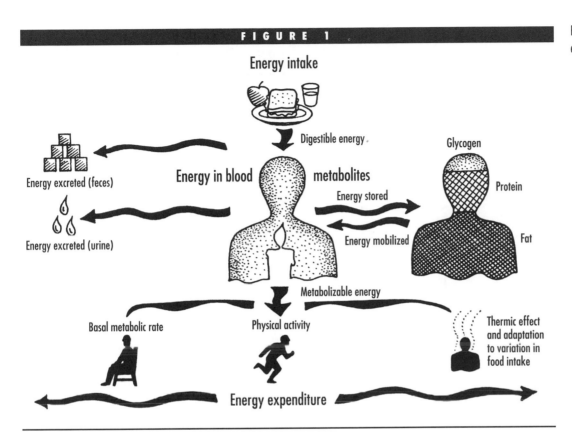

FIGURE 1

Energy intake

Digestible energy

Energy excreted (feces)

Energy excreted (urine)

Energy in blood metabolites

Energy stored

Energy mobilized

Glycogen

Protein

Fat

Metabolizable energy

Basal metabolic rate

Physical activity

Thermic effect and adaptation to variation in food intake

Energy expenditure

What Is Basal Metabolic Rate?

The amount of energy expended by a fasting person completely at rest (but awake) prior to getting out of bed for the day is defined as basal metabolic rate or BMR. The relationship between BMR and total energy expenditure is depicted in fig. 2. For a sedentary person, BMR accounts for about 60-70 percent of daily energy expenditure; the remaining 30-40 percent is from physical activity and from body heat produced after a meal. Physical activity is responsible for as much as 50-60 percent of total energy expenditure in people who include frequent aerobic exercise into their lifestyle.

How Is Energy Expenditure Measured?

In the research or hospital setting, energy expenditure is determined by examining

Components of
energy expenditure for
a sedentary person

FIGURE 2

5–10% Thermic effect

30–40% Physical Activity

60–70% Basal metabolic rate

inhaled and exhaled air and measuring the person's oxygen consumption and carbon dioxide production. The ratio between oxygen consumption and carbon dioxide production is called the respiratory quotient or RQ. Daily energy expenditure in kilocalories is calculated from an equation that accounts for the number of units of oxygen and carbon dioxide exchanged by a person under specific conditions. This technique for measuring energy expenditure is called indirect calorimetry because it measures heat production (calories) indirectly from respiratory gas exchange.

In the United States, a number of laboratories have built room-sized indirect calorimeters. One of these, at the ARS laboratory in Beltsville, MD, is shown in the photograph. Volunteers stay in the room for a total of 24 hours. During this time they are served meals and snacks, and they have access to a TV, VCR, telephone, desk, chair, bed/couch, and toilet facilities. While this technique accurately determines energy expenditure, the physical activity of the volunteers is typically lower than their normal daily physical activity because they are confined to the room calorimeter.

Scientists have recently turned to a technique called doubly labeled water ($^2H_2{}^{18}O$) to estimate the energy expenditure of free-living human volunteers. This technique requires volunteers to consume small amounts of water that contain the nonradioactive isotopes of hydrogen and oxygen—deuterium (^2H) and oxygen-18. Each volunteer's rate of excre-

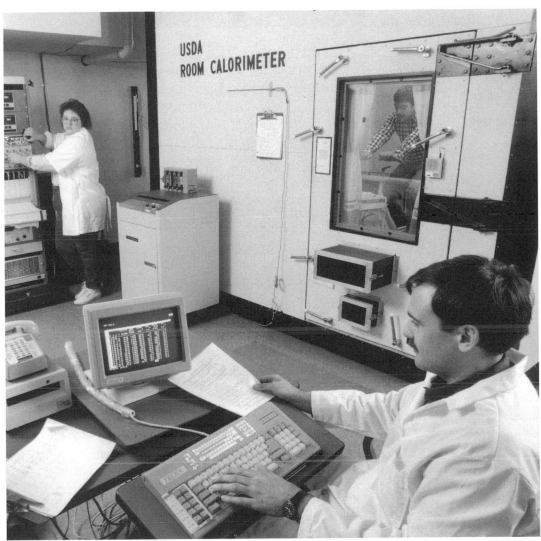

A calorimeter with a human study volunteer in operation at an ARS Laboratory in Beltsville, MD.

USDA ROOM CALORIMETER

USDA/1287X1310-17

tion of deuterium and oxygen-18 is measured in daily spot urine samples for 14 days to estimate carbon dioxide production and oxygen consumption. From these two determina- tions, energy expenditure can be determined in individuals who have been free to go about their daily activity. This technique has suc- cessfully estimated individual energy expen-

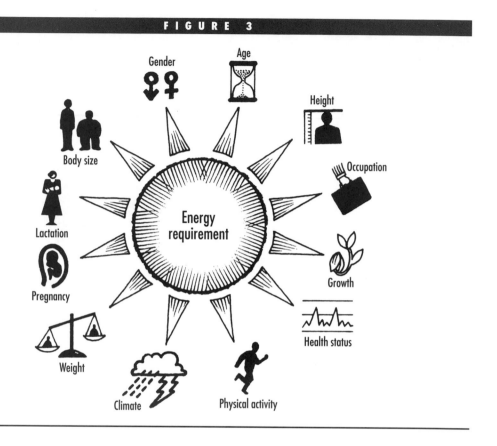

FIGURE 3

diture and is currently being used in many laboratories around the country.

How Is Energy Stored in the Body?

Like a combustion engine, the body utilizes fuel (food and drink) for energy and combusts the fuel to give energy, water, and carbon dioxide. In a car excess fuel (gasoline) is stored in the gasoline tank; in humans, excess fuel is stored in the body. When energy intake exceeds energy requirements, the energy is stored within the body as glycogen and fat.

Glycogen is the storage form of carbohydrate in the body. Both liver and muscle are capable of synthesizing glycogen and breaking it down when energy is needed for muscle and liver function or other purposes. Since glycogen is a large molecule, it cannot be stored within the muscle or liver in great quantities. Energy is stored in the body primarily as fat.

When fat is stored, it is stored in adipose tissue by two processes: hypertrophy and hyperplasia. The primary form of storage during early childhood is hyperplasia, an increase in the number of adipose tissue cells. During puberty and adulthood, adipose tissue cells change in size with weight loss or weight gain. If weight is gained, they increase in size by hypertrophy, the process of enlarging adipose cells to accommodate additional fat. If weight is lost, then the fat is mobilized from the adipose tissue cells and the cells decrease in size.

In early childhood, energy is stored and mobilized to facilitate growth and development. Therefore it is important that the overall energy balance be positive. That is, more energy must be taken in than expended in the child's daily activity to provide energy for growth. Children increase in weight until the end of adolescence, when they reach their adult weight.

The goal for adults is to maintain this healthy adult weight and not increase it. In order to maintain weight, adults must be in energy balance; that is, their energy intake must be closely matched with energy expenditure. When energy intake exceeds energy expenditure, a person is said to be in positive energy balance and gains weight.

Within the scientific community there is currently much discussion as to the exact definition of the term "ideal body weight." The USDA-Health and Human Services 1990 Dietary Guidelines are one of many sources that suggest healthy body weights.

Am I an "Apple" or a "Pear"?

During the last 10 years, researchers in Europe and America have gathered data in large populations of men and women to demonstrate the importance of the location of fat on a person's body. They found that the risk for disease (cardiovascular disease, hypertension, and diabetes) and premature death increases in obese populations that have greater deposits of fat around their abdomen (or waist) than around their hips. This distribution of fat is typical of obese males and is named "android" or "apple." Women typically have more fat deposited around the hips and buttocks than around the abdomen. This distribution pattern is named "gynoid" or "pear."

To determine whether you are an "apple" or a "pear," you must first know your waist-to-hip ratio (WHR). This ratio is determined by dividing the waist circumference measurement by the hip circumference measurement. Men having a WHR greater than 1.0 and women having a WHR greater than 0.85 are consider "apples." Conversely, men having a WHR less than 1.0 and women having a WHR less than 0.85 are consider "pears." In people who are significantly overweight or obese, fat distribution has great significance. "Apples" have increased risk for cardiovascular disease, hypertension, and diabetes.

Most of this research has been conducted in Europeans or in Americans of European descent, and it is not certain at this time if these generalizations hold true for African-Americans, Hispanic-Americans, Asian-Americans, or Native Americans. One ARS study found that African-American women have greater amounts of fat on their upper bodies than European-American women. Further research is being conducted in ARS and other laboratories to see if these generalizations concerning disease risk are applicable to the whole American population.

Recent research studies have found that within the abdominal region, location of fat can be predictive of disease and premature death. Fat located just below the skin is called subcutaneous fat, while fat surrounding vital organs is called visceral fat. While most people with a high WHR have larger deposits of visceral fat than those with a low WHR, some people with high WHR have their fat located more subcutaneously. In epidemiological studies, large deposits of visceral fat in the abdominal region (near the waist) have been associated with greater risk for disease and premature death.

Can I Change My WHR or Fat Deposition Pattern?

In ARS and other research studies, magnetic resonance imaging (MRI) has been used to determine the location of fat within the abdominal region and also to monitor fat loss during a weight-reducing regimen. When a person loses weight, fat is lost from all over the body. However, the largest amount of adipose tissue will be lost from the regions of the body having the largest adipose tissue deposits at the beginning. This means that if one has large fat deposits on the buttocks and hips, these regions will lose the most fat. At the end of a weight-losing regimen, these regions of fat may still be large, but the amount of fat will be reduced. While it may be difficult to change the body's fat patterning or WHR with weight loss, some studies report small changes. The benefit of weight loss for the person with large amounts of visceral fat is the decrease in visceral fat and therefore a presumed decrease in risk for disease and premature death.

How Can I Assess My Body Composition?

While there are many sophisticated methods of determining one's body composition in the laboratory, the familiar "pinch-an-inch" test (pinching fat tissue between the thumb and forefinger) is probably the easiest way to determine the presence of fat deposits on one's body. While it may seem imprecise, it has some merit.

Is It True That the More Weight One Loses, the Harder It Is To Continue Losing Weight?

Research studies at ARS have not supported the common belief that it becomes harder to lose weight the longer one diets. In fact the decrease in energy expenditure or metabolic rate seen in dieting individuals can be explained by the decrease in energy intake and the decrease in lean tissue that is obligatory with weight loss. Perhaps the single most important predictor of one's energy requirement is physical activity, such as walking, running, swimming, cycling. Frequently this type of physical activity decreases during a weight-loss regimen.

What Determines a Person's Energy Requirement?

The amount of energy a person requires to maintain energy balance is called the energy requirement. As shown in fig. 3, many factors influence one's energy requirement. Energy metabolism can be affected by any or all of these factors, making the study of energy requirements very complex.

Bioavailability: How the Nutrients in Food Become Available to Our Bodies

David S. Wilson
Assistant Professor,
Department of Nutrition,
University of Nevada, Reno,
and
Andrew J. Clifford
Professor, Department
of Nutrition, University of
California, Davis

Bioavailability is the degree to which food nutrients are available for absorption and utilization in the body. It is a critical issue for many nutritional concerns.

Why Do We Care About Measuring Bioavailability?

The role of bioavailability is important in establishing nutrient requirements and using those requirements in food labeling. The amount of a nutrient in a food that the body can actually use may vary depending on age and physiologic condition, such as pregnancy. Nutrient availability is also important in testing and marketing infant foods, nutritional supplements, and enteral formulas (for patients who can't digest solid foods).

An understanding of bioavailability is also important because consumers continually change their dietary patterns for reasons of health, economics, or personal preference, and knowledge of nutrient bioavailability may influence their choices. Furthermore, as the range of food products from which consumers may choose constantly increases (especially with production of new and unconventional convenience foods), the food processing industry has a critical interest in the effects of food processing and preparation on the bioavailability of nutrients.

Demographic changes also expand food choices, so that determining the nutrient availability and adequacy in ethnic foods is of greater concern. The use of vitamin and mineral supplements by as many as 50 percent of Americans suggests a need for accurate data on the availability of nutrients in these supplements. Finally, nutrient-drug interactions may alter nutrient bioavailability and thus affect nutritional status in individuals who are taking certain drugs.

Analyzing and Measuring Bioavailability

Bioavailability refers to the amount of a nutrient in a food that the body may ultimately use to perform specific physiological functions.

Several factors influence the bioavailability of a nutrient. These include:
- Digestion,
- Absorption,
- Distribution of the nutrient by the circulating blood, and
- Entry of the nutrient into the specific body tissues and fluids in which it may be physiologically effective.

Bioavailability may be quantified to some extent by measuring (1) the amounts of the nutrient in various body tissues and fluids or (2) the growth or enzyme activity that depends on the nutrient. A nutrient is rarely stored in a single body tissue, however, so that determining the nutrient levels in single tissues may not accurately reflect the true bioavailability. For example, levels of nutrients in blood, which is an accessible tissue for measurement purposes, may not reflect the levels in other tissues that are the major stores, such as liver.

Changes in response variables such as growth, immune competence, or enzyme activity must also be validated by comparison

A lifelong habit of drinking milk is associated with increased bone mass. A consumer scans the label on a new product in the dairy section of a northern Virginia supermarket.

Ken Hammond/USDA 92BW0799-7

with other criteria, since individually they may not reflect true bioavailability. Growth, for example, does not reflect the degree to which nutrients are stored in tissues in an animal that is already fully replete with this nutrient. Selenium-dependent glutathione peroxidase activity in liver may not indicate the bioavailability of selenium for other proteins that require it. Moreover, none of these functional responses reveals much about the processing of a nutrient at the specific stages of digestion, absorption, and utilization.

Each of the steps involved in the process that makes nutrients bioavailable can be affected by a variety of factors in the food itself, and also by the nutritional status of the individual. It is particularly difficult to assess bioavailability when the nutrients are present in many different forms in foods and tissues.

As complicated as it appears to be, the assessment of nutrient bioavailability still remains critical to our understanding of how humans utilize essential nutrients from consumed foods and to our appreciation of how foods satisfy our nutritional requirements.

Researchers have found new analytic techniques that permit more accurate identification and measurement of nutrients in foods and tissues, and they have creatively applied these techniques to improve our understanding of observed variations in the bioavailability of a nutrient from different foods.

Techniques to measure vitamin and mineral levels include affinity and high-performance liquid chromatography for separation and isolation of individual nutrients; mass spectrometry for separation and identification with very high specificity; and the use of "tagged" nutrients (or isotopes, that can be chemically identified at various stages) as tracers that allow monitoring of the effects of nutrient handling at each step that may affect bioavailability. In some cases, foods can be intrinsically labeled with tagged nutrients by growing the plants or animals in the presence of tagged nutrients. This experimental approach provides a more valid or realistic model for examining nutrient bioavailability than does one that adds the tracer form of the nutrient to foods that are ingested.

Individual Nutrients and Food Factors That Affect Bioavailability

A variety of components in foods may reduce or enhance the bioavailability of the nutrients. Some components may form complexes with a nutrient and prevent its digestion or absorption or even degrade the nutrient, as is the case with foods that contain an enzyme that breaks down the B vitamin, thiamin. Protein inhibitors that often reduce nutrient bioavailability are generally destroyed by cooking. Other complexes can increase solubility and, thus, enhance absorption. Recent developments in the availability of selected nutrients are summarized below:

Calcium

Efforts to understand the metabolic and dietary factors that lead to osteoporosis, or the loss of skeletal mass with aging, emphasize the importance of calcium bioavailability. Calcium in foods exists mainly as complexes with other factors (phytates, oxalates, fiber, lactate, fatty acids) from which the calcium must be released to be absorbed.

Plant constituents of the diet, in particular, may reduce calcium bioavailability so that people who do not use dairy products are less likely to obtain adequate amounts of calcium. Oxalates, present in some foods, normally bind with calcium in the gut, and the body excretes both of them together, thus limiting calcium absorption and availability. Researchers are using plants intrinsically labeled with tracer forms of calcium to evaluate the effects of plant food constituents on calcium bioavailability. Calcium supplements are also being evaluated by these techniques to determine their availability to humans.

Recent research has shown that the bioavailability of calcium from calcium carbonate, a widely used supplement, is similar to that from milk. It has also been shown that vitamin B6 deficiency may reduce calcium availability.

Iron

Iron deficiency is widespread in the United States and is a major cause of anemia in susceptible populations, especially in those whose demand for iron is high, such as growing children or pregnant women. Many fac-

All the steps in the process that makes nutrients bioavailable can be affected by a variety of factors, including the food itself and the nutritional status of the individual. Studies with human volunteers contribute information to be used in setting Recommended Daily Allowances for trace elements.

Bruce Fritz/USDA 92BW1231-32

tors, including dietary components (phytates, tannins, phosphates, and high calcium intake), exercise, menstruation, and maturity may increase or reduce iron availability. Iron absorption and utilization increase as iron stores are depleted, but inhibiting factors in such foods and beverages as soybeans and tea can impair iron absorption. Conversely, including meat or foods containing vitamin C in a meal enhances iron absorption. It is not known how meat achieves this effect, but recent research suggests that some factors in meat form a complex with iron to increase its absorption. Meat also increases gastric acid secretion, which may increase iron availability and absorption.

The optimal criterion for measuring the bioavailability of iron is not clear. The most commonly used response criterion is hemoglobin concentration in blood. The most recent research suggests that regeneration of red-blood-cell hemoglobin (an oxygen-transporting protein) can be used to measure iron bioavailability, thereby providing an easily obtained index of iron availability. Protocols are being developed to predict the bioavailability of iron in humans based on animal models. Recent research also shows that interactions of other minerals, such as zinc and calcium, with iron may reduce iron bioavailability. Copper deficiency, cooked meat, and raw vegetables are thought to enhance iron absorption.

Copper

Copper deficiency can result in anemia, bone disease, and diminished immune competence. Excessive intake of copper can lead to toxic effects, especially vascular problems such as low blood pressure and high blood-cholesterol levels. The bioavailability of copper is affected by a variety of factors. Among those which decrease bioavailability are suboptimal levels of acid in the gastrointestinal tract; the boiling of foods, which may leach away copper; and the consumption of uncooked protein foods. Copper bioavailability may also be reduced by interaction with other minerals such as iron, zinc, lead, cadmium, and selenium.

Lead

Intake of lead has become a major public health concern. Lead toxicity is most widespread in children, in whom it may lead to impaired mental development. In poorly nourished populations, it commonly results in anemia by interfering with the availability of essential nutrients, such as iron and copper. Recent research indicates that increasing meat intake reduces lead absorption from drinking water or other sources of ingested lead. Additional copper intake is more effective than either iron or zinc in reducing lead absorption, although intake of all three minerals seems to protect against lead toxicity.

Vitamin B12

Vitamin B12 deficiency rarely occurs from inadequate dietary intake but can become a problem for the elderly, leading to serious hematologic, neurologic, or gastrointestinal consequences. With age, the stomach secretes less of a protein necessary for the absorption of B12. Research indicates that pectin and other soluble dietary fibers can interfere with absorption of vitamin B12 from foods, as well as with reuse of the vitamin made available from secretions into the intestine. Inadequate knowledge of the actions of such fibers in the digestive tract, along with dietary recommendations for increased fruit and fiber intake, indicates a need for additional research.

Folic acid (folate)

Studies implicating folic acid in birth defects from impaired development of the spinal column and brain suggest that the recommended dietary allowances need to be reexamined as more accurate data on folate bioavailability and utilization are obtained. This will be especially critical for pregnant women. The bioavailability of folate in a typical U.S. diet is about 50 percent. An examination of folate-depleted rats indicates that folate bioavailability varies from about 70 to 100 percent depending on the food source. Folic acid labeled with stable isotopes is now being used to better standardize assessments of food-folate bioavailability in humans.

Vitamin B6

Vitamin B6 occurs in several forms in foods and is necessary for normal lipid and amino acid metabolism, red-blood-cell function, hormone production, and immune competence. The forms present in plant sources may include a complex with a glucose molecule, which appears to reduce the bioavailability of other forms of vitamin B6 present in foods. The vitamin B6 present in foods from animal sources exhibits very high availability—as much as 100 percent in tuna—while availability in foods from plant sources is low, 20 to 40 percent, due in part to the presence of the complex. Vegetarians are thus at particular risk for low vitamin B6 intake. Vitamin B6 status also appears to decline with age for reasons that may include reduced absorption. Research on the bioavailability of vitamin B6 is emphasizing the effects of the glucose complex in foods.

Improving Our Food Choices

Knowledge of nutrient bioavailability is key to our understanding of the role of nutrients in maintaining human health. Improved knowledge of nutrient bioavailability can help in providing definitive, quantitative dietary guidance, and it can help us translate what we know into optimal and desirable eating patterns and food choices.

Nutrition, Brain Function, and Behavior

James G. Penland
Research Psychologist,
Grand Forks Human Nutrition
Research Center,
Agricultural Research
Service, USDA,
Grand Forks, ND

It is widely accepted that a well-balanced diet and good nutrition are necessary to ensure normal growth, prevent disease, and maintain physical performance. Despite much speculation and some important early findings about general malnutrition, relatively little is known about how specific nutrients affect the brain and other organ systems in relation to mental activities, emotional states, and behavior in healthy individuals. With few exceptions (for example, vitamin B12 and iron), the behavioral consequences of deficiency are not presently considered as criteria when establishing recommended dietary allowances. However, the involvement of a broader range of disciplines and recent methodological advances have led to the reemergence of studies on brain function and behavior in relation to nutrition. This area of research represents a unique approach to assessing the functional consequences of altered nutrition.

This chapter focuses on this nutrition research; describes current methods of assessing nutrition, brain function, and behavior; highlights several interesting findings; and discusses future challenges.

Why Study Brain Function and Behavior?

Among the public, there is a strong and persistent belief that what we eat affects our mental and emotional states and, in general, our ability to perform day-to-day activities and to meet life's demands. It seems we all have theories, or at least suspicions, about the functional importance of this or that food or specific nutrient. In fact, some of us alter our diets and take supplements and freely advise others to do likewise, with the firm belief that such changes will improve the way we feel and our ability to perform.

This belief often creates a psychological environment amenable to food faddism and uncritical acceptance of claims made by self-styled "nutritionists." Today's "smart" foods, promoted as a way to increase "brain power" and enhance memory, are a recent example. Scientific evidence to support most of these claims of the beneficial effects of specific nutrients or diets is at best conflicting and, more typically, simply lacking. The study of nutrition, brain function, and behavior responds to public interest and will, with time, produce the experimental data needed to assess the legitimacy of health claims and provide reliable criteria useful for evaluating nutritional status and making recommendations for dietary intakes.

The consumption of nutrients (biologically active chemicals), in the form of foods or supplements, affects body chemistry which, in turn, affects brain chemistry and function. Neural impulses are largely the result of sodium and potassium exchange, but numerous other minerals, carbohydrates, amino acids, proteins, and vitamins affect cell membrane permeability, neurotransmitter metabolism, and the glial cells that provide structural and nutritional support to neurons.

The delicate chemical balance of the brain is somewhat protected by the blood-brain barrier, which restricts entry of certain chemicals to the brain via the blood. Nevertheless, the brain is highly susceptible to changes in body chemistry resulting from nutrient intake and deficiency.

The brain receives, stores, and integrates sensory information and initiates and controls motor responses. These functions correspond to mental activities and form the basis for behavior. Thus, theoretically, there is a direct connection between nutrition, brain function, and behavior. Furthermore, behavior may be unique as a criterion for establishing nutritional adequacy, in that it represents the functional integration of all biological systems, including homeostatic and other compensatory mechanisms that determine the practical importance of a nutritional deficit or excess.

Who Studies Brain Function and Behavior?

In the United States, studies on nutrition and brain function are conducted at private laboratories and hospitals, academic institutions, and government research laboratories. Government-supported research in this area is concentrated in the Department of Defense (DOD), USDA, and the National Institutes of Health (NIH). DOD nutrition programs focus on enhancing performance during combat and in other stressful environments, while NIH nutrition programs focus on the brain and behavior related to disease states and drugs used in treating disease. Only USDA addresses the relationships among nutrition, brain function, and behavior in the population as a whole.

Dr. James G. Penland, ARS Human Nutrition Research Center in Grand Forks, ND, prepares a subject for testing.

USDA/0885X929-18A

One of the six principal objectives stated in USDA's 1992-98 Agricultural Research Service (ARS) Program Plan is to "develop the means for promoting optimal human health and well-being through improved nutrition" and to "define adequate and safe ranges of intake for nutrients." To meet this objective, the plan explicitly recognizes the need to acquire "information about the effects of foods and nutritional adequacy on behavior and performance."

Within ARS, the Grand Forks Human

Nutrition Research Center, in North Dakota, has been a leader in studying the effects of nutrition on brain function and behavior in both humans and animals for more than a decade. The human nutrition research centers located in San Francisco, CA, Boston, MA, Beltsville, MD, and Houston, TX, have also conducted studies in this area.

The need for broad institutional support is clear because this research is truly multidisciplinary, drawing heavily from the fields of biochemistry, physiology, neuroscience, psychology, and medicine, and, less frequently, from epidemiology, sociology, and anthropology. Technological and analytical advances have further involved the fields of biotechnology, computer science, and multivariate statistics. Coordinating and integrating the activities of scientists from these diverse fields is a significant challenge and key to successful research on nutrition, brain function, and behavior.

Important Issues To Consider

Several considerations are common to most studies of nutrition, including those on brain function and behavior. Inadequate dietary intakes result in deficiency states that occur by degree, ranging from suboptimal to marginal to severe. By definition, a severe clinical deficiency in any essential nutrient is going to have profound effects, particularly during periods of early development. However, cases of marginal or subclinical deficiencies are far more common (at least in the United States) and thus probably merit greater attention by researchers and a larger share of experimental resources.

Optimal intakes for all nutrients are difficult to determine and have not yet been established. This issue of optimal intakes is particularly important to the study of brain function and behavior, and interest arises in part from the increasing emphasis of medical and allied professionals on promoting health rather than treating illness and in part from the belief that brain function and behavior within the normal range can and should be improved.

The choice of an animal or human model is important. Animal studies permit greater control over genetic and environmental variation, assessment of effects over an entire life span and even across generations, and extensive analysis of brain chemistry and anatomy. They can also be useful in assessing brain physiology, mental processes, and some emotional responses, such as anxiety. However, there are often significant differences between humans and animals in nutrient metabolism; human brain function and cognition are considerably more complex, and the behavioral repertoire of humans, including speech, greatly exceeds that found in animals. Thus, the ability to generalize findings from animal studies to humans is limited and many aspects of function simply cannot be studied in animals.

Even within a healthy population, nutritional effects on brain function and behavior must be studied separately in numerous distinct groups. These groups may be defined by

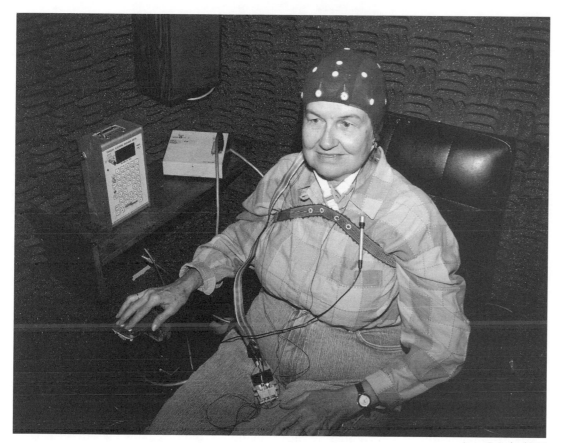

A research subject ready for testing that will measure relationships among nutrition, brain function, and behavior.

James G. Penland/ARS

characteristics such as age, sex, body composition, exercise, stress, and dietary choices including consumption of vegetarian and other restricted diets, caffeine, and alcohol. The overwhelming majority of existing studies on nutrition, brain function, and behavior were conducted on children.

The diet contains both nutrients and nonnutrients. Examples of the latter are preservatives, artificial sweeteners, and substances like caffeine and alcohol. Studies that assess the effects of excessive amounts of either nutrients or nonnutrients may be considered toxicological rather than nutritional in nature. When nutrient intakes are manipulated by supplementation, amounts can be at either physiologic (appropriate to the body's normal functioning) or pharmacologic amounts. Although pharmacologic or therapeutic amounts may be required for a brief period to remedy a severe deficiency, they are in excess of amounts that can be reasonably acquired from the typical diet.

Methods of Assessment

In experimental studies, nutrient intakes are manipulated, selected responses are measured, and other potential factors are controlled. Intakes may be modified in an acute or chronic fashion. Single-meal and short-term (weeks) supplement studies exemplify acute modifications, while long-term (months) supplement studies are examples of chronic approaches. In correlational studies, nutritional intakes and status and response variables are measured and statistically interrelated. Because intakes and thus status are not under experimental control in these studies, other factors that naturally change with intake and status may confound results and make them uninterpretable. It is essential, therefore, that experimental studies be used in nutrition research on brain function and behavior.

Nutritional status is determined by biochemical assay of biological samples (blood, urine, feces, menses, sweat, and hair) to validate the effectiveness of manipulating nutrient intakes via the diet or supplementation. In correlational studies, an estimate of intakes can be made using diaries of food consumption or recall and, along with nutritional status, serve as a predictor variable.

Brain function is assessed biochemically, physiologically, and behaviorally. Biochemical assays of blood and urine for carbohy-drates, proteins, amino acids, and neurotransmitter precursors and metabolites provide indices of changes in brain biochemistry relevant to nutritional intake and status.

The electrical activity of the brain is measured by using the electroencephalogram (EEG) under conditions of rest (the subject is given no explicit task demands) and while the subject is engaged in some mental activity, such as counting backward by 7's. EEG data are long-latency responses of the brain (greater than 1 second) and provide a measure of background rhythmic activity at rest and during task performance.

Brain electrical activity is also measured in response to auditory, visual, and somatosensory stimulation. Data collected in response to sensory stimulation are short-latency responses (less than 1 second), referred to as evoked or event-related potentials (EPs), and they index how rapidly the central nervous system responds to information-processing demands. If the subject is instructed to respond (press a button) to some stimuli but not others, the EPs index the subject's expectation, decisionmaking, and response preparation.

Behavior is assessed by measuring accuracy and response times during performance of cognitive tasks. Cognition is simply the collection of psychological processes involved in sensing, attending to, perceiving (attributing meaning), encoding, and retrieving information and using that information to solve problems, make decisions, and execute controlled responses. Cognitive processes occur in the context of and are affected by emotional or mood states, which are themselves the result of a complex interaction between physiological activation and cognitive appraisal. Although performing any activity involves most, if not all, cognitive processes, a well-designed task with multiple stimulus or response conditions or both can emphasize a single process. Different cognitive processes are associated with different patterns of electrical activity and with different regions of the brain. Therefore, performance on cognitive tasks indirectly assesses brain function while providing a direct assessment of behavior relevant to real-world activities.

Because of their subjective nature, mood states such as anger, anxiety, confusion, depression, fatigue, and sleepiness are assessed by using self-report measures. Questionnaires and tests are also used to assess nutritional effects on stress, intellectual achievement, and social behavior. However, social behavior is most commonly measured by observing and recording the frequency, quality, and intensity of contact with others.

Highlights From Human Studies

Studies of severe protein-calorie malnutrition in children have a long history and are by far the most common of any nutritional studies. They have reliably found that malnourished children have abnormal EEG's, reduced activity levels, and impaired attention. A variety of other behavioral consequences have been frequently, but not consistently, reported, including impaired or delayed mental (particularly verbal) and motor development, impaired intersensory integration, reduced academic performance, increased crying in infancy, hyperactivity, apathy, withdrawal, and impaired social skills. With rare exceptions, however, these studies were correlational in design such that brain and behavioral effects were confounded by an impaired interaction of the child with his or her social and physical environment.

An ongoing series of experimental studies has repeatedly shown that eating a high-carbohydrate, low-protein meal on an empty stomach increases the relative availability of the amino acid tryptophan, and promotes synthesis of the neurotransmitter serotonin. Under these conditions, several behavioral effects have been consistently observed: impaired attention and slowed reaction times, increased fatigue and sleepiness, and reduced pain sensitivity.

Severe deficiencies in several B vitamins have profound effects for brain function and behavior, including abnormal EEG's, impaired memory, anxiety, confusion, irritability, and depression. Subclinical deficiencies in thiamin (B1), riboflavin (B2), niacin (B3), pyridoxine (B6), cobalamin (B12), and folic acid are also commonly found in elderly and psychiatric populations. However, experimental studies have not been done to determine the involvement of individual vitamins in memory processes or in thought and affective (emotional) disorders. Experimental pyridoxine and vitamin E deficiencies produce abnormal brain electrical activity in humans and ani-

A subject's behavior is assessed by measuring accuracy and response times during performance of cognitive tests.

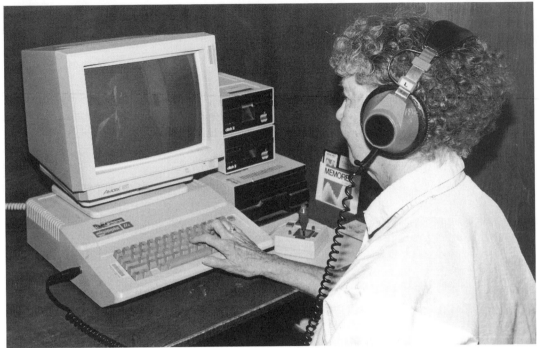

James G. Penland/ARS

mals, and vitamin C supplementation in rather large doses (1-2 grams per day) seems to influence brain activity, although in varying ways.

The relationship of iron to brain function and behavior has received considerable attention, particularly in children. Iron deficiency reliably results in impaired attention and learning, hyperactivity, and apathy, which are consistent with findings of reduced dopamine (a brain neurotransmitter) in iron-deficient animals. In several studies with young adults, iron intake and status were related to EEG and EP responses and to performance on tasks assessing short-term memory; the findings indicate that low levels of iron result in reduced alertness and impaired memory.

Supplementation and correlational studies have found increased brain and behavioral excitability with low zinc intakes and status. Subclinical experimental magnesium depletion was also found to increase brain electrical activity. Nutritional copper deficiency reduces brain excitability, consistent with reported reductions in several neurotransmitters in copper-deficient animals. Behaviorally, calcium supplementation has been related to relief of pain during menstruation.

Boron, a mineral not yet recognized as essential for humans, has shown effects on brain electrical activity and cognitive performance in several studies with older adults. When compared with higher boron intakes, EEG changes noted with low boron intake were in the direction of those found with other forms of malnutrition. Low boron intake also increased reaction times on attention, perception, memory, and motor tasks.

These highlights do not fully represent the numerous and varied studies conducted on nutrition, brain function, and behavior in humans; however, they do represent the most consistent findings. Experimental studies with animals are even more numerous, and there has been no attempt to present the findings from studies of nutritional deficiencies during pregnancy and lactation, which have profound and often lasting effects on the developing nervous system. Likewise, space limitations do not permit presentation of findings from studies on food additives, including preservatives and sweeteners, or substances like caffeine and alcohol.

Future Research

The complexity of research on nutrition, brain function, and behavior is evident, but so too is its potential to generate knowledge that has broad practical application and benefits. Future studies will no doubt identify new relationships and better characterize existing ones, while attempting to discover underlying mechanisms. Although the focus of early studies was on the effects of general malnutrition in children, future studies will more likely focus on specific nutrients and their effects on brain function and behavior in adults. Experimental (in contrast with correlational) studies offer the best hope of distinguishing nutritional from nonnutritional effects on these critical aspects of function.

It is also highly probable that future research will attempt to identify nutrient intakes that will result in optimal performance (psychonutrition). To be sure, one challenge for researchers in this area will be to present findings in a manner that tempers the public's tendency to uncritically embrace new findings before they are replicated and refined and to overgeneralize highly specific findings obtained under the controlled conditions of the laboratory.

Suggested Reading

J. Brozek and B. Schurch (Eds.), *Malnutrition and Behavior: Critical Assessment of Key Issues*, Nestle Foundation, Lausanne, Switzerland, 1984.

W. B. Essman (Ed.), *Nutrients and Brain Function*, Karger, New York, 1987.

J. R. Galler (Ed.), *Human Nutrition*, vol. 5: *Nutrition and Behavior*, Plenum Press, New York, 1984.

Nutritional Needs of the Elderly

Irwin H. Rosenberg
Director, USDA Human
Nutrition Research Center
on Aging at Tufts University,
Boston, MA

When the 21st century dawns in just a few years, one American in eight will be 65 years old or older. By 2030, the percentage of the population over age 65 is estimated to be 20 to 25 percent; that is one out of every four or five Americans. This is an enormous shift in population, perhaps the greatest in history, because the shift is occurring on every part of the globe. The magnitude of this change is emphasized when we realize that only 1 in 25 of our U.S. population was over the age of 65 in 1900.

This demographic shift presents our Nation with a most important challenge: the health and nutritional needs of a population that is growing older. Our food and food products will increasingly have to address the special needs of older Americans as they strive to maintain a high degree of function into old age. The goal is for the lives of older Americans to be not only longer but also of high quality and independent.

To meet this challenge, we must know much more about the nutritional needs of older persons and about how diet and nutrition influence the processes of aging.

Laying the Foundation

One hundred years ago, the U.S. Government—particularly USDA—began to lay important foundations for research on the relationships among diet, health, and aging. By establishing a USDA research laboratory at the Connecticut Experiment Station under the direction of Dr. Wilbur Atwater, with a fundamental commitment to understanding nutritional requirements, the United States also established its commitment to world leadership in research on human nutrition. Our life expectancy has increased dramatically over these 100 years, and we can increasingly use these scientific foundations to benefit older Americans.

A major impetus to research in this field came when the U.S. Congress in 1977 passed legislation establishing the USDA Human Nutrition Research Center on Aging at Tufts University. Its mission was to better understand the nutritional needs of the elderly and the relationships among diet, nutrition, and aging. In the 15 years since the program began, and in the 10 years since the opening of the research center building in Boston, substantial progress has been made toward meeting these national goals.

When the 10th edition of the Recommended Dietary Allowances was released by the National Academy of Sciences in 1989, there were numerous gaps in our knowledge about the nutritional requirements of the elderly. It is now expected that new knowledge in this area will have a substantial impact on the next edition of the Recommended Dietary Allowances.

Influence of Physiologic Change on Nutritional Needs During Aging

Some of the physical and physiological changes that occur during the aging processes are visible. The changes in skin texture, hair color, and body posture and shape are

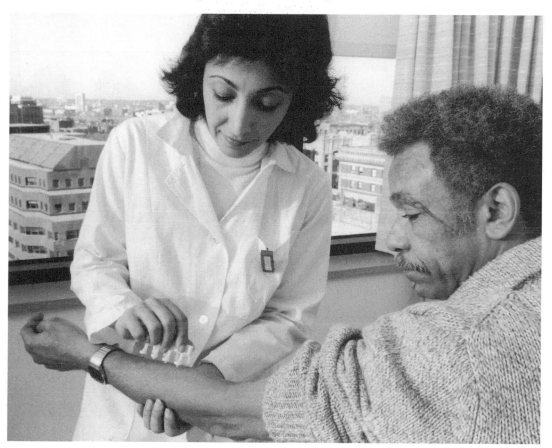

Nutritionist Simin M. Meydani administers a delayed hypersensitivity skin test to a volunteer to see if vitamin E supplements can boost the immune system in healthy older people.

USDA/0286X135-35

the most obvious. At the Human Nutrition Research Center on Aging, considerable attention has focused on the physiological changes that occur during aging. This will lead to better understanding of how these changes can influence our nutritional requirements, and also how diet and nutrition may influence or modify these changing functions.

The results are exciting and encouraging.

The more we learn about the relationships between physiologic change and diet, and about the relationships between degenerative processes associated with aging and diet, the more we are provided with opportunities to use dietary means to slow some of these degenerative processes. These processes were once considered to be inevitably associated with aging.

A researcher monitors testing to learn about nutritional needs of older people and how the diet and nutrition influence the process of aging.

USDA/92BW0404-22

Some of the physiologic differences that occur during aging and that influence requirements for nutrients are

- Changes in body composition that may result in changes in requirements for calories,
- Changes in the skin that may influence requirements for vitamin D, and
- Changes in the intestinal tract that may influence requirements for some vitamins.

Emerging research on the relationship between diet and chronic degenerative diseases of older persons holds promise for the use of diet and nutrition to treat conditions such as cataract of the eye, retinal degenera-tion leading to blindness, declining immune function, cardiovascular disease, stroke, osteoporosis, and even cancer. Although some of these findings, described below, are preliminary, overall they hold great promise of leading to effective programs for the health and well-being of aging and older Americans.

Changes in Body Composition

The most dramatic physiological transforma-tion that occurs over the decades of aging is the change of the composition of the body. As lean or muscle mass decreases, along with decreasing mass and mineralization of bone, fat increases as a percentage of body weight.

These changes can result in weaker bodies; less mobility; and some risks associated with excessive body fat, including diabetes and heart disease. Research in the last 10 years emphasized that these changes in body composition are not simply changes that are programmed to occur with aging: in fact, these changes largely reflect our habits. That is to say, an increasingly sedentary lifestyle leads to the loss of muscle mass and to an increase in fat.

An important finding of current research is that at an advanced age (even 90 and above), the appropriate forms of physical exercise and activity can reverse these changes and can result in higher percentages of lean body mass and substantially increased muscle strength. This is particularly important with respect to energy requirements with aging, because caloric needs are so closely linked to the amount of lean, metabolizing muscle mass in the body. By exercising and increasing such muscle mass, we overcome one of the important changes often associated with aging: decreased appetite. A person who is becoming more active responds with increasing appetite to meet the needs of a larger lean mass and more activity. An additional benefit of physical activity is the maintenance and even increase of bone mass.

Osteoporosis is a condition that affects mostly women beyond menopause but also men to a lesser degree. The weakening of bones in osteoporosis leads to increased risk of fracture. This important health problem relates to requirements for calcium and vitamin D, the vitamin most responsible for controlling the absorption of calcium from the diet.

Much of the natural vitamin D comes from synthesis in the skin in the presence of sunlight. Because the efficiency of this process diminishes with age, the older person increasingly depends on diet for enough vitamin D to maintain the absorption of sufficient calcium. Because these needs are not usually met by diet, the blood levels of vitamin D decline with age; with this decline, the efficiency of calcium absorption also decreases. This in turn leads to the loss of calcium from the skeleton and to osteoporosis.

Recent research indicates that by increasing the dietary intake of vitamin D, we can prevent some of the age-related decline in bone minerals. We are faced with the challenge of how to best meet the increased dietary requirements of vitamin D in older persons in order to prevent osteoporosis and bone fracture.

Another physiologic change that occurs with aging that influences nutritional requirements is changes in the stomach that result in decreased production of stomach acid. Stomach acid is important for certain digestive processes including the normal absorption of dietary vitamin B12, folic acid, and iron. Partly as a result of these changes in the stomach, a higher incidence of vitamin B12 deficiency occurs in older persons. This deficiency may be important with respect to blood formation, neurologic function, and cardiovascular function. Once again, this research may allow us to better meet the increased nutritional

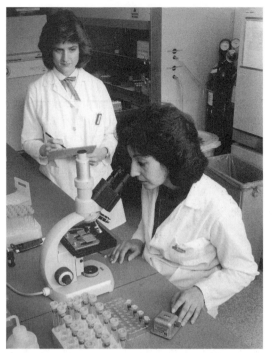

Nutritionist Simin M. Meydani (right) conducts vitamin E research, as an assistant looks on.

USDA/0286X137-26

requirements of the elderly so as to prevent the degenerative processes related to subtle dietary deficiency.

Degenerative Conditions That May Respond to Dietary and Nutritional Modification

A better understanding of the requirements of the elderly for vitamin B12 and folic acid may lead, surprisingly, to better dietary prevention of heart disease and stroke. We have heard much about the relationship between fat and cholesterol and the risk of heart disease. This knowledge has influenced the national policy on diet in a positive way. Research findings indicate that we can further control heart disease by nutritional means. Recent research shows that the amino acid homocysteine, like blood cholesterol, is a factor that contributes to the risk of coronary disease. And the blood level of homocysteine is controlled in humans to a large extent by vitamin B12, vitamin B6, and folic acid. Continuing research along these lines may provide us with other dietary means of lessening the risk of cardiovascular disease and stroke, and possibly even some of the dementing syndromes (reduced ability to reason) of the elderly.

Nutrients May Help Prevent Cataracts

The most common operation performed on older Americans is cataract extraction. Cataracts have a huge impact on the quality of life of older Americans. As we learn more about cataract formation, we better understand the interplay between antioxidant nutrients (such as vitamin C, vitamin E, and the carotenes) and the processes that damage the eye lens and lead to cataracts. Intervention studies now under way are expected to indicate the amounts of these antioxidant nutrients in our diets that may retard the onset of cataracts. Similar but much more preliminary studies relate antioxidant nutrients with senile degeneration of the retina, the leading cause of blindness in the elderly.

Like the lean body mass, the mass and function of the body's immune system decline

90

with age. This is extremely important because the immune system is critical in the body's defense against infection, cancer, and other conditions. Promising research findings indicate that some of the decline in immune function associated with aging can be changed or reversed by increasing the intake of nutrients such as vitamin B6, zinc, and vitamin E. Some of this research may lead to a better understanding of how these and some other nutrients (including antioxidant nutrients) in our diet may help to prevent certain forms of cancer.

Building on Our Research

These are a few examples of the accumulating research findings that are providing the scientific basis for reconsidering some of the nutritional requirements and dietary goals for the elderly. Scientifically based programs to influence the dietary and physical activities of aging Americans can have an enormously positive impact on their health, well-being, independence, and quality of life. USDA research over the last 100 years appears to be providing a rich harvest in this area.

Developing Research Talent for the Future

Lois Ann Davis
Education Specialist,
Office of Higher Education
Programs, Cooperative State
Research Service, USDA,
Washington, DC

The process of nutrition research is ongoing. Researchers at USDA facilities, the private sector, and universities continue to search for more and more complete information about the foods we eat, how foods affect our health, and how to improve the quality of the foods we eat—and thus, the quality of our lives. Research on genetic factors affecting our health is a crucial component of the ongoing research.

One USDA program that encourages young research talent is the National Needs Graduate Fellowships Program administered by the Office of Higher Education Programs, CSRS. This grants program was initiated in 1984 at the urging of business and industry

Researchers at USDA facilities, the private sector, and universities continue to search for more and more complete information about the foods we eat. Sally Alexander (left) and Anthony Hadley test rice varieties at the University of Arkansas at Pine Bluff.

Scott Bauer/USDA 93CN1359

leaders. It is targeted specifically to recruiting and training outstanding predoctoral students for critical scientific positions. Six areas of national need, which have shortages of expertise, have been identified under the program. These areas include Human Nutrition and Food Science.

The fellows supported by this program have been engaged in important research projects, and some of them have made significant breakthroughs in their fields. Following are some examples of important projects conducted by fellows at three different universities.

The University of Georgia has an outstanding program in genetic research relating to obesity and diabetes. Michael McIntosh, now a graduate of the program, has been researching the antiobesity-antidiabetic actions of a naturally occurring steroid, dehydroepiandrosterone (DHEA), which produces estrogen and testosterone, two important hormones for both men and women. The hoped-for result of the research is the development of methods to increase the production of the steroid during adulthood, thereby increasing protection against developing obesity, diabetes, cancer, and elevated blood lipids. McIntosh has written some 12 publications on this topic.

Another former USDA fellow supported by the University of Georgia, Gary Truett, has completed his doctoral degree. He has shown that the gene for obesity in obese Zucker rats is identical to that in obese rats of other strains and in obese mice. The fact that there is a cross-species similarity in this gene is

Research on genetic factors affecting our health is a crucial component of the ongoing research.

Keith Weller/USDA 93CN1360

exciting to researchers. Other species will have to be examined, but it is possible that such a gene can be found in humans. If that proves true, then research can be done seeking ways to prevent its expression.

Martin Hulsey, a graduate student and fellow at the University of Georgia, has been interested in the control of food intake and has found a unique anorectic factor in adipose (fat) tissue that affects feeding behavior. He has partially isolated and characterized this factor. Proctor and Gamble has expressed interest in this work and has agreed to fund a postdoctoral project for its continuation. If the factor can be identified, it may be a powerful pharmacologic agent in treating obesity.

Still another graduate student at the University of Georgia, Berry Jordan, is studying aberrations in proteins in the mitochondria of diabetics. (Mitochondria, sometimes called the powerhouses of cells, are critical for energy production in the cells.) These mitochondrial protein abnormalities may contribute to the metabolic problems experienced by diabetics. Jordan has found that feeding saturated fat turns on the synthesis of these proteins, which in turn contributes to the development of the diabetic state.

An obese rat as compared to a normal rat was part of the research of a former student at the University of Georgia, Gary Truett. He has shown that the gene for obesity in Zucker rats in identical to that of obese rats of other strains and in obese mice.

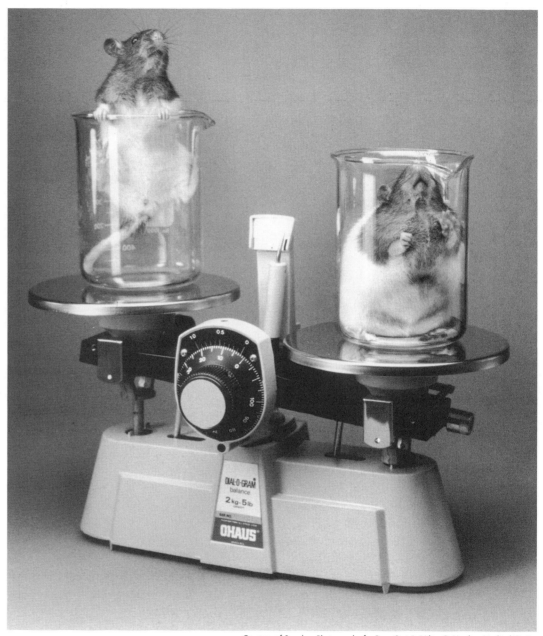

Courtesy of Socolow Photography for Penn State's Milton S. Hershey Medical Center

Tuskegee University has supported a research program to study the effects of nutrition on behavior. Helen J. Herndon, a graduate student there, has studied the relationship between lipid status and academic performance of college students. She found that college students often develop poor eating habits, substituting foods high in fat and calories for more nutritious food choices. Demographic variables, such as education, nutrition knowledge, socioeconomic status, age, sex, and race, have been shown to influence food consumption patterns among college students and other students. The results showed that when lipid levels increased, food energy level increased. Therefore, low food energy intake may be considered a consequence of low total lipid intake. These findings may have implications for the eating behavior of university students across the Nation, especially those at predominantly black institutions.

USDA fellow Anne Kepple, at Cornell University, is performing research that focuses on community nutrition and the role that research and information play in the formulation of food and nutrition policy at the local level. The goal is to analyze the relationship between food insecurity (a lack of access by all people in a community through normal food channels to enough nutritionally adequate food) and selected risk indicators that have implications for public policy. It is hoped that results of the research will help nutrition professionals use information more strategically to form food and nutrition policy.

These studies were all initiated as graduate research supported by USDA. The achievements of these talented young scientists suggest the ongoing contributions that food and nutrition research can make in improving Americans' lives.

Contributors to this chapter include Carolyn D. Berdanier, Professor of Nutrition, University of Georgia, Athens; Michael K. McIntosh, Assistant Professor of Nutrition, University of North Carolina, Greensboro; Martin G. Hulsey, Research Associate, Department of Foods and Nutrition, University of Georgia, Athens; Roy J. Martin, Professor and Chair, Department of Foods and Nutrition, University of Georgia, Athens; Helen J. Herndon, Assistant County Agent, Alabama Cooperative Extension Service, Hamilton; Ralphenia Diggs Pace, Head, Department of Home Economics, Tuskegee University, Tuskegee, AL; Eloise Carter, Associate Director of International Programs, Tuskegee University, Tuskegee, AL; Anne Kepple, Graduate Student, Division of Nutritional Sciences, Cornell University, Ithaca, NY; and C. Garza, Director and Professor, Division of Nutritional Sciences, Cornell University, Ithaca, NY.

Domestic
Food Assistance
Programs

PART 3

Feeding America's Future: USDA's Child Nutrition Programs

Stanley C. Garnett
Director, Child
Nutrition Division,
Food and Nutrition
Service, USDA
Alexandria, VA

Only children who eat well can learn well. And only children who learn well can build the future.

USDA's food assistance programs recognize the inseparable links among health, nutrition, and educational success; therefore, a number of programs are specifically for children. The continuum of care begins with the Special Supplemental Food Program for Women, Infants, and Children (WIC), which serves the Nation's youngest children who are at nutritional risk. Other child nutrition programs pick up from there.

The Child Nutrition Programs administered by USDA's Food and Nutrition Service (FNS) are designed to give children access to a more nutritious diet, to improve their eating habits through nutrition education, and to encourage the consumption of foods produced by American farmers. Many of these programs benefit the Nation's most needy children.

Long-Term Commitment

As early as 1853, the need for child feeding programs was recognized in the United States. Initial efforts to provide school food services were sporadic yet persistent, and they culminated in the establishment of the National School Lunch Program in 1946.

Over the years, as the National School Lunch Program grew in public and nonprofit private schools and institutions, program operations became more sophisticated, and the relationships among nutrition, health, and educational success became more pronounced. In addition, several other school feeding programs were established to fill in gaps in the nutritional needs of school-age children.

The School Breakfast Program was established to offer a nutritious breakfast in schools. The Special Milk Program for Children was designed to encourage the consumption of milk by children in schools. The Summer Food Service Program (SFSP) was created to provide a food service program during the summer months when school was not in session.

While the nutritional needs of school-age children were being addressed, those of preschool children were not. The Child and Adult Care Food Program (CACFP) was developed to address the nutritional needs of children in child care centers and family day care homes. The WIC Program was also created, to focus on the nutritional needs of pregnant women, infants, and young children at home.

Over the years, each of these programs has undergone changes to accommodate new research in nutritional health and education trends, while maintaining a commitment to providing nutritional food to keep children healthy enough to learn.

The National School Lunch Program

The National School Lunch Program (NSLP) makes free or low-cost lunches available to about 25 million children each school day in approximately 93,000 schools throughout the Nation. More than half these children get their meals free or at a reduced price. The program is available to 98 percent of public school children, and to 90 percent of all school children.

At the turn of the century, a penny lunch program was started in Philadelphia. A program in rural Wisconsin schools provided lunches for children prepared in the homes of women and heated in pint jars set in a bucket of water on top of a stove.

The Depression of the 1930's spurred the growth of school feeding programs. Widespread unemployment meant less money for food. At the same time that the market for farm products declined and surpluses grew, many children were going hungry.

In 1935, new legislation authorized USDA to buy price-depressing surplus foods. Needy families and school lunch programs provided outlets for those commodities. In a separate action, under the Works Progress Administration, the preparation and serving of school lunches became a source of employment.

The expansion in school feeding programs seen in the 1930's slowed in the 1940's. World War II resulted in the growth of defense industries which provided work for many. The huge requirements for food to support the armed services resulted in fewer commodities being available to school lunch programs. The threat to school feeding programs activated a number of groups concerned with such issues as children's health, the disposal of surplus agricultural commodities, the effects of consolidating rural schools in the South, jobs, and the fact that many men rejected for military service had health problems related to nutritional deficiencies.

In 1946, these concerns converged when Congress enacted the National School Lunch Act, "as a measure of national security, to safeguard the health and well-being of the Nation's children, and to encourage the domestic consumption of nutritious agricultural commodities and other food."

Participating schools receive cash assistance and donated foods from USDA, which serve to lower the cost of the meal to the paying child. Schools are provided with more than 60 different kinds of food including meat, fruits and vegetables, fruit juices, vegetable shortening, peanut products, vegetable oil, and grain products such as flour.

In return, participating schools must serve lunches which meet the minimum meal pattern requirements, and they must offer those lunches free or at a reduced price to needy children. The lunch pattern specifies the minimum amount of five food items a school must offer to receive Federal reimbursement: meat or meat alternate, bread or bread alternate, milk, and two fruits and/or vegetables. Efforts are being made to serve more nutritious, healthful foods. Schools have been provided new recipes which emphasize reductions in sugar, fat, and salt, and many improvements have been made in the foods provided by USDA.

A Special Milk Program for children encourages consumption of milk by children in schools. A student at Bailey's Elementary school in northern VA enjoys a container of milk.

Ken Hammond/USDA 93CN0711-16

The School Breakfast Program

The School Breakfast Program (SBP) makes low-cost breakfasts available to more than 5 million children in nearly 55,000 schools and institutions each school day. It is not as widely offered as the school lunch program and is more likely to operate in schools where economic need is greater.

As in NSLP, participating schools receive cash assistance to lower the cost of the breakfast to the paying child. In addition, the schools have access to the donated foods made available under the NSLP.

Participating schools must serve breakfasts which meet the minimum meal pattern requirements, and they must offer breakfast free or at a reduced price to needy children. The breakfast pattern specifies the minimum amounts of four food items a school must offer in order to receive Federal reimbursement: a serving of fluid milk, a serving of fruit or vegetable or both, and two servings of bread/bread alternate or meat/meat alternate or one serving of each.

Grants from USDA over the last 4 years have encouraged schools to start breakfast programs. More than 6,000 schools and a million children have been added to the program since the startup grants were first issued in 1989.

The Special Milk Program for Children

Expansion of the school lunch and breakfast programs, which include milk, has led to a reduction in the School Milk Program (SMP) since its peak in the late 1960's. Participation is now limited to schools, summer camps, and child care institutions that have no federally supported meal program, or to prekindergarten or kindergarten children who attend half-day sessions and have no access to meal programs provided by the schools. Low-income children may, at local option, qualify to receive their milk free.

The SMP encourages the consumption of fluid milk by children in over 10,000 schools and institutions which do not participate in any federally assisted meal service program.

Schools and institutions may choose from

Ken Hammond/USDA 92CN0715-36

Only children who eat well can learn well. And only children who learn well can build the future. An elementary school teacher in northern Virginia uses the Food Guide to teach her students about nutrition.

among pasteurized fluid types of unflavored or flavored whole milk, lowfat milk, skim milk, and cultured buttermilk. All contain vitamins A and D at levels specified by the Food and Drug Administration.

The Summer Food Service Program

The Summer Food Service Program (SFSP) funds meals and snacks for children in needy areas—where at least half the children come from families with incomes below 185 percent of the Federal poverty level—when schools are not in session during the summer. More than 1.9 million children participate in the SFSP.

The meal service can be sponsored by public or private nonprofit school food authorities, residential camps, colleges operating the National Youth Sports Program, units of State and local government, and private nonprofit organizations that meet specific criteria.

In areas where schools operate year-round, the SFSP may be available at times other than summer. The Ninth Street School in Los Angeles, for example, offers SFSP at other times of the year. Of the 555 children attending the school during the 1991-92 school year, virtually all participated in the lunch program, and three-quarters of the chil-

The School Breakfast Program makes low-cost breakfasts available to more than 5 million children in nearly 55,000 schools and institutions each school day. Children at Bailey's Elementary School in northern Virginia begin their school day with the breakfast program.

Ken Hammond/USDA 93CN0689-4

dren participated in the breakfast program. Most of the children ate free meals.

Until recently, the school operated on the standard, single-track school year. Children were offered breakfast and lunch during the summer months through the SFSP. When the school switched to a year-round system, the children who were out of classes, or "off track," were left without a meal program. To remedy this, a local organization worked with the school district to develop an "off track" meal program which provided children who

Ken Hammond/USDA 93CN0710-27

The Summer Food Service Program was created to provide a food service program during the summer months when school was not in session.

were on break with two meals each school day through the SFSP, even if "summer break" occurred in November or March.

The Child and Adult Care Food Program

The CACFP is the fastest growing of FNS' food assistance programs, with 1.9 million children and nearly 30,000 adults served in 1992.

The CACFP provides funds and USDA-donated foods year-round to help provide meals to children up to age 12 in day care centers, family day care homes, and afterschool care programs. It also provides support for meals served to impaired and elderly adults in nonresidential care centers.

All participating institutions must serve meals which meet the meal pattern requirements specified in program regulations. Centers and family day care homes may be approved to receive assistance for up to three meals per person per day, at least one of which must be a morning or afternoon snack. In addition, centers may be approved to receive assistance for three meals and one snack or two meals and two snacks for children maintained in care for 8 hours or more per day.

Food and Nutrition Service Programs Serving Special Populations

Philip K. Cohen
Chief, Program
Administration Branch,
Food Distribution Division,
Food and Nutrition
Service, USDA,
Alexandria, VA

Approximately 1 in every 10 Americans benefits from the Food Stamp Program, USDA's largest food assistance program. However, USDA also offers other, less widely known food programs that serve special populations. These include the Special Supplemental Food Program for Women, Infants, and Children (WIC); the WIC Farmers' Market Nutrition Program (FMNP); and the Food Distribution Program on Indian Reservations (FDPIR), all administered by USDA's Food and Nutrition Service. The Administration on Aging in the U.S. Department of Health and Human Services oversees the Nutrition Program for the Elderly (NPE) with financial and commodity support from USDA.

Special Supplemental Food Program for Women, Infants, and Children

WIC's goal is to improve the health of pregnant, breastfeeding, and nonbreastfeeding postpartum women; infants; and children under 5 years old, by providing supplemental foods, nutrition education, and access to health services. Eligibility is determined by income (185 percent of Federal poverty income guidelines or below, or participation in the Aid to Families with Dependent Children, Food Stamp, or Medicaid Programs). Applicants must also be at nutritional risk as determined by a health professional.

Each month, more than 5 million participants receive vouchers that can be redeemed at retail food stores for specific foods that research has shown are rich sources of the

Maria Foster of Springfield, VA, was having a difficult pregnancy. When her weight fell to 85 pounds, she entered the hospital. She was soon discharged, 5 pounds heavier. But weight was not all she had gained. Rebecca King, a nutritionist at the hospital, counseled Foster on nutrition and immediately enrolled her in WIC, which allowed her to stretch her limited earnings as a domestic helper to include many of the foods she needed during her pregnancy. The monthly food package for pregnant and breastfeeding women includes milk, cheese, eggs, cereals, and peanut butter, dry beans, or peas.

King continued to advise her on nutrition during her pregnancy, specifically on the importance of WIC foods in her diet. Instead of the small, sickly infant she originally feared she might have, Foster gave birth to healthy 7-pound, 7-ounce Cindy Vanessa. Foster followed King's advice and breastfed her baby. While she breastfed, she continued to participate in WIC, and thus to receive the high-protein foods she required for nursing.

nutrients frequently lacking in the diet of low-income mothers and children.

The program nurtures new mothers who breastfeed, so that they can stay healthy and successfully nurse their babies. Infants and children receive foods that will help them grow and prepare them to learn in school.

WIC also provides nutrition education, which helps participants to form good eating habits, and refers them to other local health and social services.

A recent study showed that women who participated in the WIC program during their pregnancies had lower Medicaid costs for themselves and their babies than did women who did not participate. Each dollar spent in prenatal WIC benefits was found to be more than offset by reduced Medicaid costs for both mother and baby after birth. For every WIC dollar invested in pregnant women, between $1.77 and $3.13 in Medicaid costs is saved for newborns and their mothers. For newborns only, the savings range from $2.84 to $3.90.

WIC works, but it does not work alone. WIC is a "gateway" program. Many people enter the social service system through WIC. During their first visit to the WIC clinic, they learn about other programs designed to meet their needs, such as the Food Stamp Program, the Aid to Families with Dependent Children Program, and the Medicaid Program. At all levels, WIC staff work closely with other agencies that provide complementary services to participants, including prenatal care, infant and childhood immunization, and alcohol and drug abuse counseling. Through the WIC Program, USDA has also assumed a leading role in the promotion of breastfeeding, which is generally the best way to nourish infants.

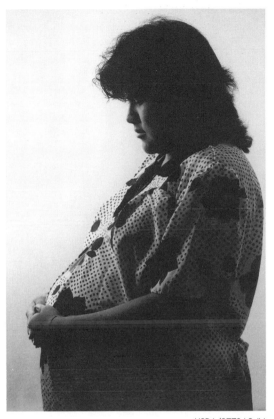

USDA/27724-2 #4

WIC's goal is to improve the health of pregnant, breastfeeding, and nonbreastfeeding postpartum women; infants; and children under 5 years old, by providing supplemental foods, nutrition education, and access to health services.

WIC Farmers' Market Nutrition Program

In some areas, WIC recipients can participate in USDA's newest food assistance program, the WIC Farmers' Market Nutrition Program (FMNP). The program began in 1992 and provides WIC participants with coupons that can be used to buy fresh fruits and vegetables at authorized farmers' markets.

The WIC program nurtures new mothers who breastfeed, so they can stay healthy and successfully nurse their babies.

Jack Dykinga/USDA 89BW0470-6

WIC participants receive $10-20 a year in FMNP coupons, in addition to their regular WIC food benefits. They can use the coupons to buy produce from farmers who have been authorized by the State to accept them. The State agency also provides nutrition education to encourage FMNP recipients to improve their diets by adding fresh fruits and vegetables and to advise them in preparing the foods they buy with FMNP coupons.

In 1991, USDA and the Wind River Indian Reservation in Wyoming added a new nutrition education initiative to the FDPIR menu. USDA's Expanded Food and Nutrition Education Program (EFNEP), administered by the Extension Service, provided a 3-week basic nutrition training course at the University of Wyoming for two aides hired from the reservation. The aides returned to the reservation to conduct cooking demonstrations, hold nutrition workshops, and counsel individual families in their homes.

Through home counseling, nutrition aide Val Whiteman taught Josephine Lynch, of the Arapaho Tribe, to deal successfully with a serious health condition. Lynch was overweight and required insulin injections to control her diabetes. Whiteman helped her to improve her diet, and she lost 57 pounds. Her eyesight also stabilized. Through proper nutrition, Lynch also ended the need for injections. Her doctor could prescribe oral medication instead, and he considered her diabetes to be under control. Other Indian tribal organizations are adapting successful efforts like the Wind River initiative to their own tribal environments.

The FMNP is now authorized in certain areas of 11 States: Connecticut, Iowa, Maryland, Massachusetts, Michigan, New York, North Carolina, Pennsylvania, Texas, Vermont, and Washington. New State agencies will be added as funds become available.

Prepared dinners at the Prince William Senior Center in Woodbridge, VA are made ready for delivery through the Meals on Wheels program.

Ken Hammond/USDA 93BW0056 12A

States that choose to operate the FMNP must contribute at least 30 percent of the total cost of the program.

Food Distribution Program on Indian Reservations

The Food Distribution Program on Indian Reservations (FDPIR) provides an alternative to the Food Stamp Program (FSP) for low-income Native Americans. In 1974, Congress mandated operation of the FSP in all counties nationwide. At that time, many Native Americans expressed a preference for continuation of the Needy Family Commodity Distribution Program, through which they had traditionally received food assistance. They indicated that the remote location of most reservations makes it difficult to participate in the FSP.

Food stamp offices, as well as grocery stores where Food Stamps can be transacted,

Congregate meals are prepared by Annie Smallwood (left) and Mary Linstrom at the Prince William Senior Center in Woodbridge, VA.

Ken Hammond/USDA 93BW0059-8

are often located far from where Native Americans live. Furthermore, the few, smaller stores characteristically found in such remote rural areas tend to have higher prices, thus reducing the purchasing power of Food Stamps. In response to these concerns, Congress established the FDPIR as an alternative to Food Stamps in 1977. Eligible households cannot participate simultaneously in both programs, but may switch from one to the other on a monthly basis. The program is administered by States and Indian tribal organizations.

Nutrition Program for the Elderly

Established by the Older Americans Act of 1965, the Nutrition Program for the Elderly (NPE) provides prepared meals to persons at least 60 years old and their spouses regardless of age. Eligibility is based solely on age; a means test is not required. USDA provides per-meal support in the form of commodities or cash for meals that average one-third of the Recommended Daily Allowance of nutrients. Projects must serve at least one meal a day for 5 or more days each week, except in rural areas, where States can approve less frequent meal service.

NPE offers congregate meals served in recreation centers or other facilities and "Meals on Wheels" delivered directly to the

Hazel Carter (left) receives her hot meal from Daphne Van Tiem at her home in Occoquan, VA. Her meal was delivered by the Meals on Wheels program.

Ken Hammond/USDA 93BW0057-20

homebound elderly. Many older Americans are not able or inclined to cook for themselves, and they may live in relative isolation. Congregate feeding addresses both of these tendencies by providing nutritious meals in a social setting. Meals on wheels responds to the needs of the frail and homebound elderly, who might otherwise have no alternative but an extended-care residential facility.

A Sturdy Safety Net— Food Stamps

Richard G. Woods
Assistant to the
Deputy Administrator,
and
Carol S. Stobaugh
Food Program Specialist,
Food Stamp Program,
Food and Nutrition
Service, USDA,
Alexandria, VA

May 29, 1961, marks the beginning of today's Food Stamp Program. On that day, Mr. and Mrs. Alderson Muncy of Paynesville, WV, bought a can of pork and beans at Henderson's Supermarket. They were the first in the Nation to be issued modern Food Stamps and to use them to purchase food for their family. McDowell County, WV, was one of eight sites beginning "pilot programs" for Food Stamps in 1961. The pilots were intended to discover whether this method of helping poor families to buy food would work.

Mr. and Mrs. Muncy had no idea what they were inaugurating. No one could have predicted just how successful the program would become. In 1992, 25 million persons, on average, received Food Stamps each month. Approximately 1 in 10 Americans received some assistance from Food Stamps, making the program one of the most enduring and effective safety nets for Americans in economic distress.

How It Works

Food coupons, or stamps, are used to supplement the food buying power of eligible low-income households. The program is administered nationally by USDA's Food and Nutrition Service (FNS) and locally by State welfare agencies.

Available under the same rules and restrictions in every State and all counties in the United States, the Food Stamp Program is recognized as a potential source of help by most Americans. Grocers throughout the Nation understand the program, appreciate the additional purchasing power it has given their poorer customers, and regularly deposit redeemed Food Stamps in their local banks. The Federal Government, through the USDA Food and Nutrition Service, makes these deposits good. Most important, recipients of Food Stamps realize that this system allows them great freedom in choosing those foods they believe are most useful to their families and in choosing where they wish to shop.

Farmers and food processors benefit because their products can be purchased by people who otherwise might not be able to buy enough food. Studies show that Food Stamps substantially increase the nutrients in home food supplies, including such important problem nutrients as calcium, vitamin C, and iron.

The program is flexible and convenient. Unlike the direct distribution of canned goods and other foods to individuals in distress, which often occurs after disasters, the Food Stamp Program requires no special warehouses, inventories, or trucks to distribute food. As long as there are participating grocery stores with food stocks, recipients can redeem their stamps. When economic times are tough, the program expands to provide help to all those who are eligible. When times are better, and the unemployed gain jobs, the program shrinks accordingly.

Using uniform rules, local welfare office workers examine each applicant's income, assets, and family characteristics to make sure that only those in need receive stamps. Persons who are found to be guilty of fraud

USDA/0175W30-13

25 million people, on average, receive Food Stamps each month. Approximately 1 in 10 Americans receives some assistance from Food Stamps.

are made to repay their benefits, and disqualified from further participation. Grocery store owners who sell ineligible items (such as liquor, tobacco, cosmetics, and other nonfood items) for Food Stamps also lose the privilege of participating in the program.

Grocers or individuals who traffic in Food Stamps, buying them from poor persons at a fraction of their face value and redeeming them through a bank, face prosecution, possible imprisonment, and permanent disqualification from the program. States that become lax in administering the program, granting undeserved benefits to applicants, wind up owing the Federal Government sizeable amounts of money; a quality control system finds errors.

Eligibility

To get Food Stamps, someone in the household fills out an application form at the nearest welfare office. Once this is done, an interview with an eligibility worker takes place. At the interview, the applicant provides documents verifying such factors as income, assets, employment status, and age of each member of the household. Benefits are geared to household size, a household being those persons who regularly prepare and eat food together.

Loney Fontenot (right), Louisiana Rehabilitation Services, assists Cynthia Bowling (left) of New Iberia, LA, with an emergency Food Stamp application after Hurricane Andrew. Unlike the direct distribution of canned goods and other foods to individuals in distress, which often occurs after a disaster, the Food Stamp Program requires no warehouses, inventories, or trucks to distribute food.

Bob Nichols/USDA 92BW1515-12

The key eligibility factors are assets and income; tests are in place to assure that households with high income and large amounts of assets do not qualify for the Food Stamp Program. Some assets are not counted, such as a home and lot. Some vehicles are not counted as assets, such as those used to produce income most of the time. For other vehicles, the fair market value is determined, and everything above $4,500 counts toward the limit on assets.

Special deductions from gross monthly income may be applied. There is a deduction that encourages people to work or keep working by counting only part of their earnings as income. This deduction results in a smaller reduction in their benefits than they otherwise would get because of their increased income. There are other deductions for dependent care, excess medical expenses for the elderly and disabled, and excess shelter costs.

Once the eligibility worker has verified that the applicant household has less than the allowed $2,000 in countable resources (it is $3,000 for households with at least one person 60 or older), and has net income within the specified limits, the applicant may be certified to receive Food Stamps. The net monthly income limits and maximum Food Stamp allotments for each family size are as follows:

Household size	Net monthly income limits*	Maximum Food Stamp allotments*
1	$ 568	$ 111
2	766	203
3	965	292
4	1,163	370
5	1,361	440
6	1,560	528
7	1,758	584
8	1,956	667
Each additional person	+199	+83

For the 48 contiguous States and the District of Columbia. There are different income limits and maximum allotment amounts for Alaska, Hawaii, Guam, and the Virgin Islands. These amounts are in effect through September 1993.

Gordon Baer/USDA 0884X1112-22

Low-income shoppers face tough decisions when spending their Food Stamps. They need to get the maximum nutrition at the lowest cost.

Delivery of Food Stamps

The eligibility worker determines the appropriate amount of Food Stamps which will be issued. Beginning with the date of application, the State has no more than 30 days to deliver benefits. (Where the household is very needy, benefits must be made available within 5 days.)

Some States issue eligible households Authorization to Participate cards, which are exchanged for the appropriate amount of Food Stamps. Other States mail the Food Stamps to the household. Still other States use a photo identification system in issuing Food Stamps. Once they are received, the Stamps may be used by the household at any authorized retailer whenever it is convenient.

Spending Food Stamps

Retail food stores must apply to the Food and Nutrition Service in order to be allowed to receive Food Stamps. When a store is authorized, it is given identifying signs and decals to post and any program participant may spend Food Stamps there. Special care is taken by the Food and Nutrition Service to make certain that enough retailers are authorized in low-income areas, so that poor people will have access to food. There are currently about 210,000 authorized stores.

The Food Stamp customer may use stamps only for food and for plants and seeds to grow food for the household. Food Stamps *cannot* be used to buy:

- alcoholic beverages
- tobacco or cigarettes
- household supplies, soaps, and paper products
- medicines or vitamins
- any other nonfood items
- food that will be eaten in the store
- hot foods that are ready to eat, such as barbecued chicken
- pet foods

Sales tax cannot be charged on eligible items purchased with Food Stamps. Any ineligible items purchased by the Food Stamp customer must be paid for in cash. These provisions help ensure that poor households receive enough nutritious food.

Food Stamps are issued in booklets of $1, $5, and $10 coupons. The grocer can give cash change only up to 99 cents. Change in even dollar amounts is given in Food Stamps.

Changes in Eligibility

Each Food Stamp household is periodically re-examined to make sure it is still eligible. In addition, Food Stamp households are required to report changes in their circumstances (such as a new job and income or more household members) which might affect their benefits. Benefits may be adjusted upward or downward appropriately.

Food Stamp recipients have rights and responsibilities, which are carefully explained when they are certified. People who break Food Stamp rules may be disqualified from the program, fined, imprisoned, or all three. If a person is disqualified, the first time is for 6 months; the second time is for a year; and the third time is permanent.

Households may continue to receive food stamps as long as they remain eligible. Children in these families are automatically eligible for free school lunch and breakfast.

The Average Food Stamp Household

A summer 1991 study of Food Stamp households showed that slightly more than half the recipients were children. The average food stamp household size was 2.6 persons with an average monthly gross income of $472 and an average monthly net income of $261; half the households had gross monthly incomes of less than $500. Almost 77 percent of all households had no countable assets and another 18 percent had countable assets of $500 or less. Those food stamp recipients who were able to work were working or otherwise meeting the work requirement—for example, by being in training or receiving education.

Food Stamps, then, go to the neediest Americans in those households with little or no income. And the Food Stamp Program does serve as a safety net: half of all recipients are on the program for 6 months or less.

Using Food Stamps for Good Nutrition

Low-income shoppers face tough decisions when spending their Food Stamps. More than most Americans, they need to get the maximum nutrition at the lowest cost for their stamps and the money with which they supplement them. Many are astute shoppers, buying generic brands and using discount coupons. Others are not as knowledgeable.

The Food and Nutrition Service makes publications available for distribution to Food Stamp recipients with information about shopping for low-cost nutrition. These publications discuss using food labels to make smart choices, the economy of preparing food rather than buying convenience foods, meal planning, cooking for one or two persons, and building a better diet. In addition, many major food chains distribute free publications with shopping advice.

If a particular nutrition problem exists in a State, that State can add a special nutrition education component to its annual Food Stamp operating plan. Federal funds are available to pay half the expenses of these components, and States are encouraged to take advantage of this opportunity to better serve Food Stamp recipients.

Access to Food Stamps

The increase in Food Stamp program participation during recent years clearly shows that the program responds to changes in the economy and in the circumstances of individual households, enabling those who need Food Stamps to get them. State and local governments have exerted tremendous effort to ensure that people in need receive the benefits to which they are entitled. In many cases,

USDA/DN3364

With so many Food Stamps in circulation, there are greater opportunities for the unscrupulous to undermine the Food Stamp Program by fraud.

they have done so in the face of reduced State and local budgets.

Some numbers illustrate the ease with which the program absorbs the newly eligible: Average monthly participation in the Food Stamp Program increased from 18.8 million in 1989 to 25.8 million in 1992—an increase of 7 million persons and 37 percent in 3 years.

Aside from active and compassionate administrators, several program features make access easier. These include:

When the recipient buys food at the grocery store, all eligible Food Stamp items are totaled by the grocer. Electronic benefit transfer (EBT) recipient Augusta Woodall likes the plastic card better than the paper food coupons.

Marian Wig/USDA 90BW1674-26

- Applicants must be given an application and allowed to file it the first day they contact a Food Stamp office. If the applicant cannot come to the office, the application must be mailed.
- States can combine the application process for the Food Stamp Program with that for other assistance programs. This saves the applicant the time and inconvenience of completing two or more applications, possibly at different locations.
- In cases where the applicant is homebound, handicapped, or otherwise unable to visit the office, an authorized representative may be appointed to represent the household in certification interviews or to get and use Food Stamps.
- If the household can't come to the food stamp office and can't appoint an authorized representative, interviews can be conducted by telephone, or an eligibility worker can be sent to the home. Face-to-face interviews can be waived for households where all members are 65 or older or are mentally or physically handicapped.
- Households in which all members receive Supplemental Security Income (SSI) can be certified through Social Security Offices, saving the household a trip to the Food Stamp office.

Electronic Benefits Transfer

One of the problems caused by growth in the Food Stamp Program is the difficulty of handling so many Food Stamps. Currently, about 4 billion new food stamps are distributed each year. This means that a special currency (hard to counterfeit) must be produced, stored in safe quarters, and transported by armored car to locations all over the United States where it can be stored and prepared for distribution in the correct amounts to eligible participants. Food Stamps must be available at the State and local levels when they are needed by recipients, so the process of moving stamps around is a big job.

Once the Food Stamps have been spent in grocery stores, each store must count and bundle its Food Stamps (usually each day) for redemption at a bank. The bank must also count and handle the Food Stamps as it prepares them to be submitted to the Federal Reserve Bank, which, in turn, pays the local bank. Finally, the Food Stamps must be sent to a central location for accounting and destruction. This process is costly and time-consuming.

With so many Food Stamps in circulation, there are greater opportunities for the unscrupulous to undermine the Food Stamp Program by fraud. A crooked retailer can lure Food Stamp recipients into giving up $100 worth of food purchasing power by offering, say, $50 in cash for the stamps. This sort of wrongdoing not only undermines the nutritional purpose of Food Stamps but also results in an illegal gain by the retailer, who deposits the stamps in a bank account. It is difficult to prevent such fraud and abuse from occurring when there are so many stamps and so many recipients.

One way to counter these problems is the electronic benefit transfer (EBT) system. EBT makes food assistance funds available to the household in a special account which can be used only by the household in approved grocery stores to purchase food.

The Food Stamp office enters the household's benefit amount in the special account each month. When the recipient buys food at the grocery store, all eligible Food Stamp items are totaled by the grocer. A plastic card (like a credit card) is passed through a reader by the recipient. Next, the recipient verifies the purchase by entering a private personal identification number into a keyboard at the checkout stand.

Both the amount of purchase and the identification number are electronically sent to the central account, and the purchase is deducted from the account. Only the total amount available in the account can be spent for food. Only a recipient with a correctly coded card and the right personal identification number can have access to that particular account. Each time the recipient makes a purchase, a receipt is provided showing the amount purchased and the remaining balance. No money or Food Stamps are involved. Each month the Food Stamp office replenishes the benefit dollars available in the account if the household is still eligible.

Currently, there are five EBT demonstration projects, located in Reading, PA; Ramsey

Recipients find EBT easier to use and less time-consuming than food stamps. They particularly like using the card; unlike Food Stamps, it does not overtly identify them to other store customers as food stamp recipients.

Marian Wig/USDA 90BW1674-16

County (St. Paul), MN; Bernalillo County (Albuquerque), NM; Linn County (Cedar Rapids), IA; and Maryland, which operates a State-wide system. A sixth EBT project is underway in Dayton, OH, where the off-line approach is being tested. In an off-line system, benefit information is stored in a computer chip in the card itself and purchases are deducted directly from the card at the supermarket terminal.

Early experience suggests there may be a number of advantages to EBT:

- No Food Stamps are involved, and accounting for benefits can easily be accomplished. Problems of transportation and storage are eliminated.
- Retailers like the elimination of Food Stamp handling and the ease and speed of settlement with the bank.
- Banks are pleased that EBT eliminates their coupon issuance role and reduces their costs for handling and redeeming benefits.
- Recipients find EBT easier to use and less time-consuming than food stamps. They particularly like using the card; unlike Food Stamps, it does not overtly identify them to other store customers as food stamp recipients.

Reporting on a June 2, 1993 "town hall meeting" held by Vice President Gore in St. Paul, MN, the *Washington Post* noted,

"Mary Jass, 35, moved here from California three years ago. She still receives welfare assistance, but without an affront to her dignity, she said.

'We happened to live in a more affluent city and most of the people in the grocery store were not me. And I would get out my Food Stamp coupons and, kind of trembling, tear them out. I wanted to get this done with, and then they had to stamp every one of them. And it was very embarrassing and I didn't like it at all and I ended up going to other stores where I wouldn't be known. Coming to Minnesota it is entirely different. No one knows, it seems, that I'm even on welfare. They think it's a credit card.'"

Welfare Reform

Many Food Stamp households receive other public assistance as well. For these families, surviving on welfare means dealing with several different Government offices and program requirements, a confusing and time-consuming task. FNS is actively working with other Government programs, such as Aid to Families with Dependent Children (AFDC), Medicaid, and the Department of Housing and Urban Development (HUD), to find ways to simplify these programs for the recipients. Concepts such as "one-stop shopping" and using the same or similar eligibility requirements for different programs are being tested.

A major stumbling block is the fact that each public assistance program is authorized by a different law, often by different committees in Congress. This makes change a slow process, but each time Congress reviews a program, changes are proposed to make it conform to the others. They are debated and often accepted.

It is now widely recognized that Government assistance may be a necessity for some recipients, not a preferred way of life. Greater attention and effort are being devoted to breaking the chains of public dependency for those who are able to do so. Work requirements for the able-bodied are part of the Food Stamp Program, as they are for several other programs.

Incentives for persons on welfare to gain the education, skills, and experience they need for successful self-support through employment are being built into programs. A number of States are experimenting with ways to more effectively integrate welfare recipients into the mainstream of American life, and we may learn from these experiments which paths to follow in the years ahead.

Helping Low-Income Americans With USDA Commodities

Alberta C. Frost
Director, Supplemental
Food Programs Division,
and former Director,
Food Distribution Division,
Food and Nutrition
Service, USDA,
Alexandria, VA

Every day, thousands of low-income people have a nutritious meal prepared with USDA commodity foods. Sometimes these meals are prepared at home; other times the meals are served at schools, soup kitchens for the homeless, day care centers, summer camps, senior centers, hospitals, nursing homes, and half-way houses for battered women or recovering substance abusers. In dollar terms (about $1 billion annually), the USDA commodity programs are small compared to other domestic food assistance efforts such as the Food Stamp or National School Lunch Programs. However, their reach is great.

A Depression Program
Through its commodity programs, the USDA has been providing food to people and help to farmers since the Great Depression of the 1930's. It was then that the Federal Government began to buy surplus crops from farmers to stabilize agricultural markets and guarantee producers a fair return for their labors in the face of eroding consumer purchasing power and dislocations in foreign trade. Although the emphasis then was on the removal of surpluses from the market, by 1938 USDA was distributing $54 million dollars worth of food annually to local public assistance agencies that gave it to the poor.

Schools also received surplus commodities to help them provide nutritious meals for millions of students who were unable to pay for their school lunches. This marrying of interests between helping the American farmer and providing for the food needs of

Every day, thousands of low-income people have a nutritious meal prepared with USDA commodity foods

Ken Hammond/USDA 93BW0033-6A

120

Sometimes the meals are prepared at soup kitchens for the homeless.

Kan Hammond/USDA 93BW0035-12A

low-income people has continued to varying degrees throughout the history of the commodity programs.

The Delicate Balance

Today, USDA provides regular commodity support to a wide variety of low-income people through eight different programs:

- The Child Nutrition Programs
- The Nutrition Program for the Elderly
- The Commodity Supplemental Food Program
- The Charitable Institution Program
- The Program for Summer Camps
- The Food Distribution Program on Indian Reservations
- The Emergency Food Assistance Program
- The Soup Kitchen/Food Bank Program

Commodity assistance is also available to victims of natural disasters.

Sometimes these commodities are surplus foods and their purchase plays an important role in stabilizing agricultural markets. This is true for some of the commodities that are provided to the Child Nutrition Programs and the Emergency Food Assistance Program (TEFAP), and all of the commodities donated to the Charitable Institution Program. For

Scott Robbins, Charlie Company, 50th Signal Corps, assists in preparing food distributed by the Food and Nutrition Service to Hurricane Andrew survivors.

Bob Nichols/USDA 92BW1507-25A

other programs—such as the Commodity Supplemental Food Program, the Food Distribution Program on Indian Reservations, and the Soup Kitchen/Food Bank Program— funds appropriated by Congress are intended to purchase commodities specifically tailored to the needs of recipients. In these instances, surplus removal gives way to other considerations such as the particular nutritional needs of program participants.

Surplus food is not lower in quality or less appealing than other food. Over the years, USDA has donated millions of pounds of meat, poultry, fish, fruits, vegetables, grain, and dairy products when they were in surplus. Purchase specifications require high quality standards; all commodities are processed using on-site USDA inspection to assure that purchase specifications are met.

The administrative agency, the Food and Nutrition Service (FNS), also pays attention to the Dietary Guidelines for Americans when selecting commodity foods. Over the last decade, purchase specifications have been changed: commodity canned fruits are now packed only in light syrup or natural juice, the fat content of canned and frozen meat has been significantly lowered, tuna is packed in water, and peanuts are unsalted. Commodity foods—surplus or otherwise—are under constant review to ensure that they meet current nutrition standards.

Since the passage of the Commodity Distribution Reform Act of 1987, FNS has collected annual preference information from all of its commodity program operators. This allows

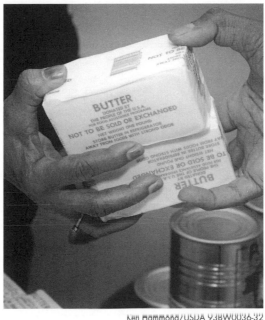

Ken Hammond/USDA 93BW0036-32

The Emergency Food Assistance Program (TEFAP) joins agricultural surpluses, USDA support for the food needs of low-income people, and the efforts of volunteer groups.

FNS to determine whether the foods it provides will be consumed once they are distributed.

Working Together

The commodity programs represent a successful melding of the interests of American agriculture and the people who need assistance in obtaining a nutritionally adequate diet. However, other important partners in this effort include State and local governments, a variety of nonprofit institutions, and thousands of volunteers.

Commodity foods are served to senior citizens in many different settings—including senior centers, churches, and Meals-on-Wheels programs—through the Nutrition Program for the Elderly. Low-income Native

In Duluth, MN, the Damiano Center not only provides food, shelter, and clothing, but also offers the homeless an opportunity, through its Handy Hands job program, to earn some much needed money at a community day labor program. If workers prove reliable, Handy Hands helps with references that can lead to full-time employment.

"Damiano Center is based on the belief that the best hope for eliminating hunger is in actively working with people, enabling them to provide food for themselves," says Jim Dwyer, who coordinates the Emergency Food Assistance Program (TEFAP) at the center. "Once their basic food needs are met, we try to create opportunities for low-income people to learn to be more self-reliant."

In Boston, more than 120 volunteer groups donate or help with meals at the Pine Street Inn for the homeless. In addition to providing food and shelter, Pine Street has an onsite clinic and provides clothing, a work rehabilitation program, permanent housing services, and a special program for women who have been chronic substance abusers and their children. This special program for women works in tandem with USDA's Supplemental Food Program for Women, Infants, and Children (WIC).

At Baltimore's Bayard Street recreation center, police officers volunteer to cook meals and help the children learn social skills and positive values.

Americans receive commodities as an alternative to the Food Stamp Program on 223 reservations throughout the country. In FY 1992, approximately 2.1 billion meals were served through the Charitable Institution Program by more than 14,000 nonprofit institutions— such as hospitals, food pantries, nursing homes, and shelters for the homeless—using surplus commodities. Over the years, USDA has provided foods such as rice, pasta, peanut butter, dairy products, flour, fish, vegetables, and fruits to these institutions.

Low-income children also receive the benefit of as many as 90 different commodity foods through the National School Lunch Program, the Child and Adult Care Program, and the Summer Food Service Program. In school year 1992-93, FNS gave school meal providers 14 cents worth of commodities for every meal served in the National School Lunch Program.

These efforts require State agencies to develop and maintain systems for warehousing and distributing commodities to local distributing organizations. State governments play a critical role in the operation of the commodity programs. Several of the programs are also heavily dependent on the efforts of local nonprofit organizations and volunteers.

All over the country, volunteer groups provide community-based services to low-income adults and children. And foods donated by USDA and private sources help them meet basic needs. Once those needs for shelter and food are met, people can turn their attention to other things that will help them become self-reliant and productive. A study of groups providing meals to the homeless, completed in 1989, found that "the higher proportion of USDA commodity foods that a provider gets, the more calories, protein, and carbohydrates are present in meals served, and the more food groups are present in the meals."

The Emergency Food Assistance Program

The Emergency Food Assistance Program (TEFAP) joins agricultural surpluses, USDA support for the food needs of low-income people, and the efforts of volunteer groups. TEFAP began in December 1981 as a special distribution of cheese to reduce large dairy surpluses at a time of high unemployment. Subsequently, other surplus commodities—such as flour, butter, nonfat dry milk, rice, honey, and cornmeal—were added to the distributions. Volunteer groups and local governments in all States provided the people needed to give out these foods every month to low-income households who needed supplemental food assistance. At TEFAP's peak in 1987, community action agencies, food pantries, churches, senior centers, and welfare offices distributed $850 million in commodities.

Today, these large surpluses do not exist. TEFAP continues because in 1989 Congress passed the Hunger Prevention Act, which provided USDA with $120 million a year for the purchase of nutritious foods to augment those that remained in surplus. In addition, the Hunger Prevention Act created a new commodity program, the Soup Kitchen/Food Bank Program. In 1992, USDA purchased $32 million in commodities primarily for those organizations that serve meals to the homeless. When States find that they cannot use all of the commodities allocated to them to meet the needs of the homeless, they can give them to food banks for distribution to other low-income clients.

The funds appropriated by Congress allow USDA to purchase a wider variety of foods for both TEFAP and the Soup Kitchen/Food Bank Program. Canned meat, peanut butter, juice, fruit, vegetables, and rice are among the commodities available. Without the surpluses of overproduction, the program is smaller now than it has been. Now it is much more common for the 17,000 local distribution sites across the country to integrate USDA foods with those obtained from private sources. In some States, food banks are now the primary source of USDA foods. In these situations, needy households can go to a food pantry or other local nonprofit organization whenever they have an emergency need for food, rather than having to wait for the scheduled TEFAP distribution.

The Commodity Supplemental Food Program

The Commodity Supplemental Food Program (CSFP) operates at 47 sites in 20 States and one Indian Tribal Organization. It provides specially tailored commodity foods to supplement the diets of low-income pregnant, postpartum, and breastfeeding women and their

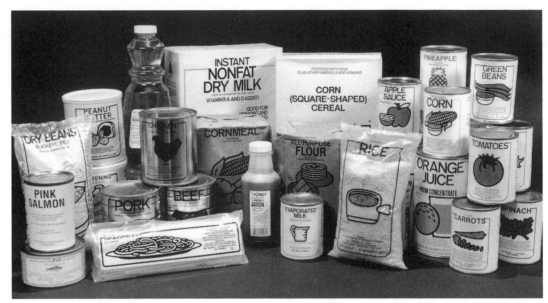

Bob Nichols/USDA 92BW1936-17

children up to age 6. In some sites, the program also serves elderly persons. The goals of CSFP are similar to those of the Special Supplemental Food Program for Women, Infants, and Children (WIC), but it provides food rather than a voucher for the purchase of food. Clients cannot participate in both programs during the same month.

CSFP started in 1968 as the predecessor to WIC, and it served approximately 342,539 participants last year. The food packages are tailored to meet the needs of women and children. The packages include such items as juice, infant cereal, infant formula, nonfat dry milk, fruits, vegetables, and canned meat. Like many other USDA commodity programs, it is heavily dependent at the local level on the efforts of nonprofit organizations and volunteers.

Sites in Denver, Des Moines, and Detroit use a supermarket concept to provide efficient and educational service to their clients. At these sites, clients are provided with a shopping list of eligible foods and are then responsible for selecting from commodity foods those items and quantities that match family ages and numbers. Nutrition education, including food preparation demonstrations, is available to help CSFP clients make food choices.

In Des Moines, a well-baby clinic that offers immunizations, lead-poisoning screening, and iron-level blood tests is also housed on the premises. Denver has begun an innovative "Food for Thought" program through which children can get children's books provided by private donations.

Since it began its CSFP operation in Detroit, Focus: Hope, which was originally formed as a civil rights organization, has been able to garner support from private and public sources to offer high technology job training to inner city residents. "The USDA food assistance available through CSFP has made it possible for us to realize our mission of eradi-cating racism, poverty, and injustice through practical and intelligent action," says Eleanor Josaitis, cofounder of Focus: Hope. "There's a lot more left to be done, but our partnership with USDA is so vital to the basic well-being of the 85,000 women, babies, and elderly citizens we serve each month. A stable source of good food allows people to start addressing other life issues that can lead to self-reliance and a brighter future for their children."

Gleaning

Nancy Leidenfrost
National Program Leader,
and
Rita Rogers
Public Affairs Specialist,
Extension Service, USDA,
Washington, DC

In an age when thousands of Americans go without food every day, it is distressing to note that up to 20 percent of the American harvest each year is left to rot. It is hard to imagine that thousands of cans and packages of edible food in canneries, packing houses, food markets, and restaurants are routinely cast aside. Yet, research has found this to be the case.

Why the waste? Often produce may not meet market standards due to shape, size, or quantity. Other times, produce may not be harvested due to a lack of farm labor. Overproduction, dented cans, broken boxes, and expired marketing dates are more reasons

"Gleaning" is an organized activity to collect unused food to be distributed to those in need. Ralph Harris collects bread from the ACCESS warehouse in Medford, OR.

Ken Hammond/USDA 93BW1031-24

why perfectly edible food is disposed of. The challenge is how to retrieve this discarded, yet edible, food and distribute it to the needy. The answer is known as "gleaning."

"Gleaning" is an organized activity in which hundreds of people collect unused and discarded food and provide it to those in need. Through gleaning, needy individuals, including low-income and unemployed persons, can receive agricultural products from farmers, processors, or retailers without charge. There are many groups, such as food banks and other charities involved with feeding the poor, that organize volunteer gleaning programs. During recent years, some USDA agencies have become key players in the gleaning effort.

Section 1774 of the Food, Agriculture, Conservation, and Trade Act of 1990 includes a Gleaning Clearinghouse provision. This authorizes the Secretary of Agriculture to provide information and technical assistance to public and nonprofit groups that want to participate in gleaning projects. The Cooperative Extension System (CES), through its national educational network, is providing information to interested groups and individuals on ways to conduct gleaning programs. Extension has served as a resource on the Executive Council of Feeding Sites—bringing food providers and the "hunger and poverty network," the public, and other groups together. Extension field faculty also provide information to farmers and growers on gleaning legislation and to producers and processors about the needs of the poor.

Agricultural products are received from farmers, processors, or retailers without charge. Harold Silver and Louise Swindler sort and inventory onions prior to distribution.

Ken Hammond/USDA 93BW1033-10

Active State Programs

A 1992 CES survey of State gleaning efforts showed that 23 States had some form of gleaning program. The wide range of State gleaning activities includes setting up soup kitchens to preserve excess food, helping to train Master Food Preservers, and providing technical assistance on food preservation. CES staff members also serve as liaison with the State Department of Agriculture.

In Georgia, excess, prepared, and perishable foods are being collected from food service donors and distributed to feeding sites. Extension then contacts the recipients, encouraging them to sign up for a program of their interest, such as the Expanded Food and Nutrition Education Program (EFNEP).

Professionals at Oregon State University's Agriculture Experiment Station take a different approach to gleaning. They arrange for teams from the Gleaning Network, Inc., a three-county effort in Oregon, to glean the garden at the Experiment Station in Medford, OR, as well as the Master Gardener areas. For years, it has been a cooperative effort boasting positive results.

"All of our gleaning team members fall within USDA poverty guidelines," said Carol

Master Food Preserver Debbie Garcia (left) holds a canning class in her home in Selma, OR. Marianne Sedgwick (center) and Barbara DeVorss learn some of the finer points of food preservation.

Ken Hammond/USDA93BW1029-9

McLaughlin, program coordinator of the Gleaning Network, Inc. "They keep the gleanings they collect. Any excess is given to our organization, which then distributes it to team adoptees."

The adoptees, McLaughlin explains, are individuals who are at least 55 years old, or disabled, and who fall within the poverty guidelines. Teams are organized according to neighborhoods in Klamath, Jackson, and Josephine counties, and may consist of as few as 5 or as many as 48 households. To prepare for gleaning at the Agriculture Experiment Station and Master Gardener areas, team members must participate in a 2-day Gleaning Network training program in which they are taught how to collect produce without damaging crops.

"We usually glean between 10 and 15 times a year at the Experiment Station and Master Gardener areas. This year we collected tomatoes, onions, squash, green peppers, two varieties of corn, and three varieties of green beans." said McLaughlin.

The concept of "harvesting after the harvest" is popular in other States as well. Washington State University Cooperative Extension personnel developed a project to specially train individuals to harvest produce left in fields and orchards. A distributor from the local area emergency food banks comes directly to the fields to collect the harvest. The food banks then immediately distribute the surplus produce to homeless people or others in need of food.

Steven Garrett is the supervisor, Expanded Food and Nutrition Education Program in Pierce County, Washington State University Cooperative Extension Service. Local EFNEP personnel and volunteers do the gleaning.

"In 1992, EFNEP personnel and volunteers gleaned 160,000 pounds of leftover fruits and vegetables," reports Garrett. "We had 96 volunteers giving a total of 4,600 hours. Seventy-five percent of the food collected went to the Emergency Food Network in Pierce County, which distributed it to local food banks. The other 25 percent went to the volunteer gleaners."

Individuals who are 55 years or older, or disabled, must meet certain guidelines to be eligible to receive assistance.

Ken Hammond/USDA93BW1030-13

Training the Gleaners

Garrett recalled that prior to 1990 local farmers had been somewhat reluctant to allow gleaners on their property for fear of potential crop and property damage. In the spring of 1990, David Ottey, executive director of the Emergency Food Network, and Margaret Movius, who was then the EFNEP supervisor in the Pierce County Cooperative Extension Office, decided to train volunteers—recruited from the county's EFNEP program—in the proper way to harvest crops. They also contacted area farmers to assure them that, because of the training, their farm property wouldn't be damaged by the volunteer gleaners. As a result of this effort, more local farmers and Tacoma-area home gardeners were willing to invite gleaners onto their properties.

Besides collecting fresh fruit and vegetables for themselves and for other needy individuals, the EFNEP volunteer gleaners also have the option of taking classes in food preservation, which are conducted by an Extension volunteer food advisor.

Throughout the Nation, more and more farmers, farmers' markets, producers, retailers, institutions, restaurants, and backyard gardeners are contributing to gleaning programs, as this humanitarian effort continues to become more popular. Brochures, fliers, toll-free hotlines, and promotional videos are just some of the means by which county Extension offices are getting the word out on gleaning.

International
Nutrition
Focus on
Developing
Countries

P A R T 4

Nutritional Status of People in Developing Countries

Arthur J. Dommen
Agricultural Economist,
Economic Research
Service, USDA,
Washington, DC

It is impossible to measure accurately the number of malnourished people in the world's developing countries, where nutritional problems are most prevalent. Counting households that are malnourished in a society on the basis of their average intake of protein, calories, vitamins, and minerals is difficult enough; measuring differences in food access by members of a hungry family is even more so.

Estimates of the Number of Malnourished People

The most recent estimate of the number of people that over a period of a year do not have access to enough food to meet their energy needs was published in a 1992 joint report by the Food and Agriculture Organization of the United Nations (FAO) and the World Health Organization (WHO). It estimated that 786 million people had a chronic dietary energy deficiency in 1988-90.[1] This is the equivalent of 20 percent of the total population of developing countries.

However, the actual number of undernourished people is likely to be higher, because this estimate does not take into account (1) problems of intrahousehold food distribution, (2) people facing seasonal or acute problems of malnutrition, or (3) those with infections.

The above estimate is based on the minimum energy requirement level for adults and adolescents doing light activity, expressed as 1.54 times the basal metabolic rate (BMR), a common physiological measure of energy consumed by the human body in a fasting state and at complete rest.

Another recent study by the International Food Policy Research Institute (IFPRI) estimated that in developing countries outside of China, 595 million people are calorie-deficient.[2] The Chinese, though poor, are generally seen as being better nourished than many developing-country populations. However, no accurate nationwide data are available for China.

Other figures give a general idea of the nutritional deficiencies prevalent in developing countries. The United Nations recently estimated that some 150 million children are underweight, about half a billion women are anemic due to iron deficiency, about 20 million low birth weight infants are born each year, some 40 million children are afflicted with vitamin A deficiency, and over a billion people are deficient in iodine.[3]

Where the Malnourished Are Located

Despite the wide margin of potential error in the aggregate figures, it is clear that the nutritional situation varies greatly from one country to the next, and can change favorably or unfavorably over time. For example, in China a major surge in aggregate food availability and consumption levels occurred during the 1970's and early 1980's. This coincided with the initiation of agricultural reforms and resulting increases in food production. Estimates of China's food-deficient poor in the early 1980's range from 70 to 100 million, or less than 10 percent of the population.[4] In Africa, on the other hand, some countries lost ground in their struggle to provide their people with access to adequate food. In Rwanda, a recent estimate was that aggregate calories available per capita per day fell from 2,034 in 1986 to 1,866 in 1987 and 1,822 in 1988.[5] These figures imply a significant increase in the numbers of malnourished people in a relatively short time.

In locating the malnourished, one cannot rely on national data on aggregate food supplies or calories supplied per capita to give an accurate picture. Even when food production and imports in a country are fairly accurately known and the country's population is known within some acceptable margin of error, we are still not likely to have an accurate idea of how well nourished its people are.

We generally have limited knowledge of how these calorie supplies are distributed within the country. The sheer magnitude of the task of moving food from food-surplus areas to food-deficit areas, where presumably it will be available to feed hungry people, is usually sufficient to skew actual distribution patterns considerably. There have been a few cases where countries have followed policies of continuing to export food when some of their own people are starving, as Sudan exported sorghum during the 1984 famine. Uneven distributions of available food tend to result from uneven distribution of income.

Data collected at the household level are really essential to understanding the distribution of malnourished people in a developing country and seeing beneath the national aggregates. The simplest way to collect such

Photo Courtesy CMS Vickie Graham, USAF

The number of malnourished people in developing countries is impossible to measure accurately.

data in rural areas is to include questions about the adequacy of the household's food production in an ongoing household survey. Whelan has suggested using the subsistence potential ratio (SPR) as a cost-effective indicator of nutrition. The SPR is a ratio of the energy or protein value of the household's food production over a year to the household's energy or protein requirements over the year. Data on production and household composition suffice to calculate this SPR ratio. Whelan calls the SPR a better proxy for nutritional status than household income.[6]

The most accurate guide to locating the malnourished, however, comes from nutrition surveys in which anthropomorphic measures are used to identify malnutrition. Table 1 compiles data from nutrition surveys of the last decade.[7] Aside from being recent, the surveys claim to be nationally representative (with the few indicated exceptions), and have been verified for reliability in terms of information provided on sample size, ages, and nutrition standards used. Regional averages have been calculated for the countries surveyed by using a weighting scheme based on the country population in the year of the reported survey.

Asia is the region with the largest malnutrition problem, both in terms of the percentage of its population that is malnourished and in terms of absolute numbers. Of the eight countries in Asia with national surveys reported, seven had rates of protein-energy malnutrition in excess of 35 percent at the time of the survey, and four had ratios in excess of 50 percent. These are extremely high rates. (Data were not presented on China because no nationally representative data are available that can be interpreted according to international norms.)

Ranking second in regional malnutrition levels is sub-Saharan Africa, but with country rates that are considerably below those found in Asia. Only one surveyed country, Niger, had a rate equal to the Asian regional average.

Following closely behind sub-Saharan Africa is the Middle East/North Africa region. Egypt, with a relatively low rate of 13.3 percent malnutrition, is a large recipient of food aid and the government subsidizes food prices. Kuwait, while producing little of its own food, is one of the richest countries in the world.

In Latin America, percentages of malnutrition levels fall to single digits in several countries. Only one country surveyed, Guatemala, had a rate above 25 percent.

Who Are the Malnourished?

Within the same country, and even within the same village, people have different access to adequate food. Obviously, poor people are at a severe disadvantage when it comes to food access, whether they live in rural, food-producing areas or in cities, unless they benefit from ameliorative programs. Food access for small farmers or farm laborers may be reduced by natural hazards of crop and livestock production (drought, floods, insect infestations, epidemic diseases), or by obstacles caused by human institutions. These problems reduce people's access to food, and thus their nutritional status. Urban poor people depend on markets to buy food or to receive food assistance, and food prices affect their livelihood and nutritional status whether they purchase food or it is purchased for them.

Other groups of people especially vulnerable to malnutrition are those who face health risks from infectious diseases or inadequate sanitation. Such conditions are often linked with malnutrition. For example, in reviewing

Within the same village, poorer people are at a severe disadvantage when it comes to food access.

Photo Courtesy CMS Vickie Graham, USAF

data from two surveys in an area of Rwanda, researchers found a discrepancy between the geographic areas with a prevalence of child malnutrition and those with a high percentage of households whose average food intake provided less than the recommended daily allowance of nutrients. Two conclusions were reached: First, malnutrition is a household problem, and average figures could mask malnutrition within households. Second, malnutrition in the sample was more related to other factors, such as sanitation, than to calorie supply.[8]

Obviously, people living in areas of warfare

or civil strife are likely to have had their sources of livelihood destroyed or markets disrupted, reducing their ability to gain access to food. When such people become displaced and are forced to live in crowded refugee camps, they become more vulnerable to the complex knot of nutrition/health causes and effects that are known to result in high mortality rates. Finally, other vulnerable groups, such as pregnant or lactating mothers and small infants, can be identified just from their relatively higher temporary need for food, or certain types of food.

Beyond such readily identifiable groups,

TABLE 1

Prevalence of protein-energy malnutrition

Region/Country	Percent of children under age 5 malnourished *Percent*	Year of survey	Population *Millions*
Asia:	49.4		552.2
Bangladesh[1]	61.4	1985/6	102.4
Indonesia	51.3	1987	179.7
Laos	48.8	1984/6	3.6
Myanmar	38.0	1985	37.3
Pakistan	51.5	1985	99.3
Sri Lanka	38.1	1987	16.5
Thailand	25.8	1987	52.9
Vietnam	51.5	1986	60.6
Sub-Saharan Africa:	29.4		144.1
Burundi	38.3	1987	5.1
Cape Verde	13.6	1985	0.3
Congo	23.5	1987	2.1
Cote d'Ivoire	12.4	1986	10.7
Ethiopia	38.1	1982	40.6
Ghana	30.7	1988	14.3
Guinea-Bissau	23.4	1980	0.8
Lesotho	13.2	1981	1.3
Madagascar	32.8	1984	9.8
Malawi	30.0	1981	6.2
Mali	31.0	1987	7.6
Mauritius	23.9	1985	1.0
Niger	49.4	1985	6.6
Sao Tome & Principe	17.0	1986	0.1
Senegal	21.6	1986	6.8
Swaziland[1]	9.7	1984	0.7
Togo	24.4	1988	3.4
Uganda	23.3	1988/9	17.0
Zimbabwe	11.5	1988	9.7

Region/Country	Percent of children under age 5 malnourished Percent	Year of survey	Population Millions
Middle East/North Africa:	22.9		126.5
Egypt	13.3	1988	52.1
Iran[1]	43.1	1980	39.1
Kuwait	6.4	1983	1.6
Morocco	15.7	1987	24.0
Tunisia	10.4	1988	7.7
Yemen PDR	25.0	1982	2.0
Latin America:	9.4		349.0
Barbados	5.3	1981	0.2
Bolivia	13.3	1989	6.6
Brazil	5.1	1989	149.6
Chile	2.3	1985	12.1
Colombia	11.9	1986	30.3
Costa Rica	6.0	1982	2.4
Dominican Republic	12.5	1986	6.6
Ecuador	16.5	1987	9.8
Guatemala	33.5	1987	8.4
Guyana	22.1	1978	0.8
Honduras	20.6	1987	4.8
Jamaica	9.2	1989	2.4
Mexico	13.9	1988	84.0
Nicaragua	10.5	1982	2.9
Panama	15.7	1980	2.0
Paraguay	1.1	1982	3.6
Trinidad and Tobago	6.9	1987	1.3
Uruguay	7.4	1987	3.0
Venezuela	5.9	1987	18.2

TABLE 1—continued

Sources: Malnutrition survey data from Rae Galloway, Global Indicators of Nutritional Risk, World Bank, Population and Human Resources Department, Policy, Research, and External Affairs Working Paper, WPS 591, February 1991, table 1, pp. 6-10. Population data from USDA/ERS, WATI data base.
[1] Rural only

others may emerge as nutritionally vulnerable. Many of these are the objects of specific effects that are only now being identified and studied in detail. Household surveys, which can help in this process of study, are costly. The paucity of primary data and the large number of variables that affect nutrition serve to mask many specific nutritional problems. For example, education level, particularly of women who usually handle food in the household, is known to be correlated with the household's nutritional status because of nutrition's link with sanitation.

During the 1980's, many structural adjustment programs in developing countries reduced nutritional well-being for the poor. These programs frequently have involved the deliberate short-run reduction of demand in order to bring macroeconomic variables, such as budget deficits, back into balance. By reducing purchasing power, these programs reduced nutritional well-being in the short run—even if they provide long term benefits. Other effects, which are not so simple to detect, include such things as changing consumer food habits through currency devaluation that reduces food imports.

Sometimes, the effect on nutritional status of these policies is minimal, as when domestically produced cereals such as sorghum and millet replace imported wheat and rice, which have become prohibitively expensive. In other instances, the effects can be damaging unless measures are taken to offset them. For example, in Nigeria traditional, coastal, and brackish water fish catches fell by 52.4 per-

cent after the introduction of a structural adjustment program in 1986.[9] This was because local fishermen depended on imported outboard motors and fishing nets, the prices of which rose steeply as a result of currency devaluation. In this case, the threat to consumers' well-being was not one susceptible to remedial action by controlling staple food prices, because one class of staples had dropped out of the picture altogether.

Nutritionists believe that gender is one of the principal factors behind the high levels of malnutrition in Asian countries when compared with African countries. They point out that children's access to good nutrition in rural Asia is much more related to gender than it is in Africa. In the Indian state of Punjab, according to one recent study, youngest daughters in households with many children are often selectively deprived of both medicine and the more nutritious foods so that their brothers may be better cared for.[10] Under normal circumstances, the communal land tenure systems that prevail in Africa and the recognized role of women in food production ensure that, in African societies, children of both sexes get a more equitable distribution of the food available. This does not prevent African communities from collapsing, however, when drought and warfare wipe out their productive assets, defeat their coping mechanisms, and turn people into refugees.[11]

An important point to remember is that very short-term nutrient deficiencies can have long-lasting effects. In an urban area of Niamey (Niger) surveyed between 1985 and

1987, a very strong relationship was found between food price increases due to crop production shortfalls and undernutrition.[12] Such fluctuations may lead to sudden weight loss and serious consequences for child survival and welfare. Thus a famine can affect an entire generation in terms of its consequences on human development. Beyond the immediate human cost, there may also be a cost in terms of economic development. A number of studies have demonstrated that among rural populations where agricultural production is labor-intensive, malnourishment will in turn have a negative effect on agricultural productivity.[13]

Conclusion

This chapter has shown the difficulty of estimating the number of malnourished people in developing countries. Nevertheless, we do know that nutritional problems are widespread in these countries. Asia has the largest nutritional problems, in terms of both the absolute number of malnourished people and the percentage of the population that is malnourished. A high correlation exists between malnourishment and poverty. But within the general category of the poor in developing countries, certain well-defined subgroups, such as urban poor people and rural laborers, may be particularly affected by food price changes that make food inaccessible.

[1]FAO and WHO, Nutrition and Development—A Global Assessment, Rome 1992, table 2, p. 6.

[2]Sumiter Broca and Peter Oram, "Study on the Location of the Poor," IFPRI, Washington, DC, mimeo, 1991.

[3]United Nations Administrative Committee on Coordination—Subcommittee on Nutrition, draft report, Geneva, Feb. 12, 1991.

[4]Tong Zhong, Scott Rozelle, Bruce Stone, Jiang Dehua, Chen Jiyuan, and Xu Zhikang, "China's Experience with Market Reform for Commercialization of Agriculture in Poor Areas," International Food Policy Research Institute, Washington, DC, mimeo.

[5]Octavien Ngarambe, Gregory Lassiter, and Scott Loveridge, "Tendances de la Production Agricole et Son Impact sur la Securite Alimentaire," Services des Enquetes et Statistiques Agricoles, Ministere de l'Agriculture, Rwanda, April 1989.

[6]William Whelan, "Incorporating Nutritional Considerations into Farming Systems Research," paper presented at the Farming Systems in the Field Symposium, Kansas State University, Manhattan, KS, Nov. 1982.

[7]Rae Galloway, Global Indicators of Nutritional Risk, World Bank, Population and Human Resources Department, Policy, Research, and External Affairs Working Paper, WPS 591, Feb. 1991, table 1, pp. 6-10. This source contains explanatory notes to surveys and describes anthropomorphic measures used in locating the malnourished.

[8]Randall Schnepf, Cornell Nutrition Program, seminar in ERS, May 20, 1992.

[9]S. O. Igbedioh, "Macroeconomic Adjustment, Food Availability and Nutrition Status in Nigeria: A Look at the 1990's," Food Policy, Dec. 1990, p. 520.

[10]Monica Das Gupta, "Selective Discrimination against Female Children in Rural Punjab, India," Population and Development Review, Vol. 13 (1988), pp. 77-100.

[11]The causative importance of asset loss is emphasized in studies of actual famine situations in Africa. See, for example, Alexander de Waal, Famine that Kills; Darfur, Sudan, 1984-1985 (Oxford: Clarendon Press, 1989).

[12]UN-ACC/SCN, op. cit.

[13]Shubh K. Kumar and David Hotchkiss, Consequences of Deforestation for Women's Time Allocation, Agricultural Production, and Nutrition in Hill Areas of Nepal, International Food Policy Research Institute, Washington, DC, Research Report 69, 1988.

Composition of Diets in Nutrient-Deficient Countries

Stacey Rosen
Linda Scott
Agricultural Economists,
Economic Research
Service, USDA,
Washington, DC

Most countries have enough food to meet their people's requirements. Malnutrition, however, persists in almost all countries.

The most common form of malnutrition in developing countries is undernutrition, in which food intake is inadequate to meet the body's energy requirements. In these countries, inadequate food intake is the usual cause of specific nutrition-related diseases and is a major force behind increased rates of infection, infant mortality, reduced productivity, and shortened lifespans. An estimated 15-20 percent of people in developing countries eat too little to maintain good health. In some countries, more than 50 percent are deficient in one or more nutrients.[1]

Populations of developed countries, on the other hand, suffer primarily from overnutrition caused by eating too many calories derived from fat and refined sugar. Overnutrition is associated with a high prevalence of obesity and chronic diseases such as coronary heart disease, hypertension, and diabetes.

In most developing countries, the adequacy of food supplies at the national level does not ensure that adequate food is available at the regional, household, or individual level. Factors that can influence the ability of individuals to acquire and utilize nutrients include: local food and water availability, food prices, a country's capacity to import food, incomes and purchasing power, women's workload and education level, local customs and food taboos, sanitary conditions, and health status.[2]

Thus, because these social, political, and economic factors contribute to malnutrition, solutions require more than the provision of food and nutrients. There are interrelationships among malnutrition, poverty, and economic development.

This chapter reviews the composition of diets in developing countries and the common types of nutrient deficiencies associated with these diets. In addition, we identify factors that may contribute to improvements in food intake—such as storage, preservation, and preparation of foods. Finally, we examine domestic production and income factors that may affect nutritional status.

Defining an Adequate Diet

Nearly 50 nutrients—including water, carbohydrates, protein, fat, vitamins, and minerals—are necessary to sustain life.[3] Not all of these substances, however, are needed on a daily basis, as the human body is capable of drawing on reserves. Daily energy requirements vary widely. Individuals will often adapt to a lower caloric intake by reducing physical activity. Energy needs and nutrient requirements are thus a function of sex, age, weight, activity level, and health status. Some nutrient requirements increase significantly during periods of infection, pregnancy, and lactation. Failure to absorb nutrients from foods due to parasitic infection or other diseases can also significantly affect nutritional status. Infants and children are particularly vulnerable because of their growth requirements.

Calorie Intake in Developing Countries

Inadequate energy intake is one of the primary nutrition problems in developing countries. An estimated 350-500 million people worldwide are not consuming enough food to meet their energy needs.[4] Low calorie intake is closely related to reduced consumption of protein, vitamins, and minerals.

The average daily per capita calorie intake across all developing countries was 2,486 in 1989. Although this represents an increase of nearly 7 percent since 1980 and a 23-percent jump since 1961, Africa, as well as many countries and individuals, continue to lag far behind the developing country average.[5] Figure 1 shows changes in per capita daily calorie intake for world regions between 1961 and 1988.

Regional Comparisons

Africa continues to lag behind the rest of the developing world in calorie intake, while Latin America and Asia have increased calorie consumption dramatically since the early 1960's. Daily energy intake in sub-Saharan Africa declined in the early 1980's as the continent struggled to overcome the combined impact of drought, rapid population growth, declining per capita incomes, rising oil prices, worldwide inflation, increased debt burdens, declining commodity prices, and civil conflict.

Increased calorie intake in Asia was largely concentrated in China and the newly industrialized countries, including South Korea, Thailand, Singapore, Hong Kong, and Malaysia. In Latin America, large caloric increases

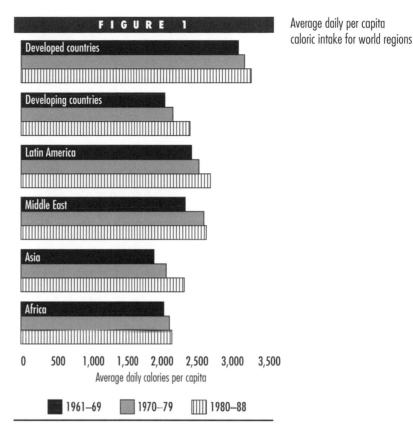

FIGURE 1

Average daily per capita caloric intake for world regions

Developed countries

Developing countries

Latin America

Middle East

Asia

Africa

0   500   1,000   1,500   2,000   2,500   3,000   3,500
Average daily calories per capita

■ 1961–69   ▨ 1970–79   ▥ 1980–88

occurred in Costa Rica and Mexico. It is important to note that these regional increases in Asia and Latin America mask many continuing deficiencies in some countries and communities. Widespread malnutrition persists within many countries in the two regions.

Staple Foods in Developing Countries

Dietary composition plays an important role in nutritional status. An ample and diverse supply of calories, protein, vitamins, and minerals is necessary for good nutrition. Diets in developing countries consist largely of carbohydrates, usually obtained from one or two staple foods. Staple foods vary by country depending on local cultures and growing conditions, but they consist primarily of cereals (such as rice, wheat, corn, sorghum, and millet) and starchy roots (including cassava, sweet potatoes, and yams). These foods are sometimes prepared with small amounts of vegetable oils and are flavored with locally available condiments, spices, and/or sweeteners.

Carbohydrates account for more than 70 percent of calories in some developing countries, compared to 40-50 percent in the developed world.[6] Diets generally lack variety and are low in fruits and vegetables, important sources of vitamins and minerals (fig. 2). This lack of diversity may be especially severe in rural areas, which have limited access to markets and thus rely heavily on a small number of locally produced food items.

The main sources of protein in developing countries are cereals, legumes, and pulses, including dried beans and peas, rather than animal products (table 1). Animal products, which account for more than 30 percent of total calories in the developed world, made up less than 9 percent of total calories in developing countries in the 1980's. Consumption of animal products was highest in Latin America, where such foods are an important part of the diet in a number of countries including Uruguay, Argentina, and other cattle-producing countries. Intake of animal foods was lowest in Africa which, with few exceptions, has a poorly

developed livestock sector and lacks the purchasing power to import such items (fig. 3).

Nutritional Value of Staples

Diets in developing countries consist of foods that have important nutritional value if consumed in adequate amounts.[7] In fact, many local foods that traditionally are prepared with a minimum of processing, such as sorghum and millet in Africa, are actually more nutritious than highly refined corn and wheat flours that are demanded in urban areas across many regions. The overconsumption of fats, a major public health problem in developed countries, is generally not a problem in developing countries, where fat intake is often inadequate. Fats account for less than 20 percent of total calories in the developing world, compared with 35-40 percent in some developed countries.

Fat intake is lowest in Asia, where it accounts for less than 16 percent of total calories. In Africa, vegetable oils, cereals, and oilcrops such as groundnuts are the main sources of dietary fats. Although cereals are low in fat, they are important sources of fat in Africa and Asia, where cereals account for more than two-thirds of dietary calories. Consumption of meat, dairy products, and animal fats, such as butter and lard, continues to increase in the developing world. Particularly in Latin America, the Middle East, and North Africa, total fat intake is likely to significantly increase.

Although protein deficiency was once thought to be a major problem in developing countries, recent research indicates that com-

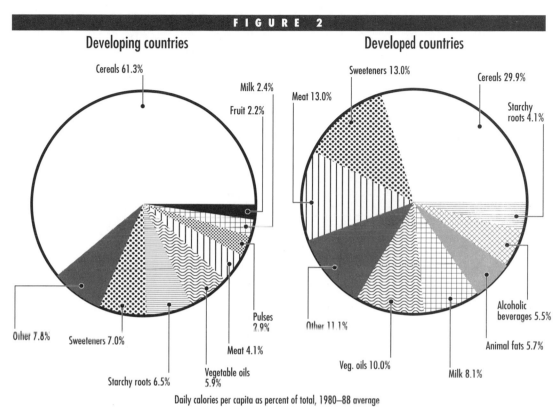

FIGURE 2

Developing countries

Cereals 61.3%

Milk 2.4%

Fruit 2.2%

Pulses 2.9%

Meat 4.1%

Vegetable oils 5.9%

Starchy roots 6.5%

Sweeteners 7.0%

Other 7.8%

Developed countries

Sweeteners 13.0%

Meat 13.0%

Cereals 29.9%

Starchy roots 4.1%

Alcoholic beverages 5.5%

Animal fats 5.7%

Milk 8.1%

Veg. oils 10.0%

Other 11.1%

Daily calories per capita as percent of total, 1980–88 average

bining cereal-based diets with small amounts of other protein foods, such as pulses, groundnuts, or animal products, can adequately meet protein needs if energy intake is sufficient.[8] One example of this would be combining rice with beans. Widespread consumption of animal products is neither necessary nor realistic given the current income limitations of large segments of the developing world, although small quantities may be useful in preventing iron deficiency, and in

ensuring adequate nutrition in children and pregnant women. Moreover, excessive intake of animal products is associated with chronic and degenerative diseases commonly seen in the Western industrialized nations.

Income Growth and Dietary Changes

While income is one of the most important determinants of diet and nutritional status, it is not necessarily true that higher incomes trans-

TABLE 1					

Major sources of protein in the diet, developing countries, developed countries, and world regions (ranked by developing country 1980-88 average)

Source	Developing	Developed	Africa	Latin America	Asia	Middle East and North Africa
Cereals	58.8	29.1	53.6	39.6	63.7	60.6
Meat	8.6	26.4	8.7	20.3	6.1	10.5
Pulses	7.4	1.7	10.4	9.9	6.9	4.3
Milk and dairy	5.6	16.7	4.7	12.5	4.1	9.2
Fish, seafood	4.1	7.3	4.8	3.4	4.2	1.7
Oilcrops	3.8	1.9	4.3	0.8	4.5	1.2
Vegetables	3.5	3.5	2.2	1.7	3.9	4.1
Starchy roots	3.1	3.2	7.7	2.9	2.4	1.2
Eggs	1.6	4.3	0.9	2.7	1.5	0.6
Offals	1.2	2.2	1.2	2.4	7.6	5.1
Fruit	1.0	1.1	1.7	2.2	0.6	2.3

Source: FAO Agrostat

late into improved nutritional status. Economic development often results in the increased consumption of fats and protein and a reduction in the quantity and quality of carbohydrates. Results of an FAO study indicate that calories from fats increased from 10 percent in low income groups to 40 percent in the highest income groups. As incomes rise, there is a decrease in calories from starchy foods (cereals, tubers), an increase in calories from refined sugar, and eventually an increase in the consumption of animal products.[9] Figure 4 shows the change in dietary composition over time in developing country regions.

Nutrition-Related Deficiencies and Diseases

The combination of low overall energy intake, dietary composition, environmental factors, and the presence of parasitic infections is responsible for many nutrition-related deficiencies and diseases. The four most important forms of malnutrition in developing countries are *protein-energy malnutrition (PEM), iron-deficiency anemia, xerophthalmia* (a condition linked to vitamin A deficiency that can lead to blindness), and *endemic goiter and cretinism*.[10]

PEM is a disease stemming from the coin-

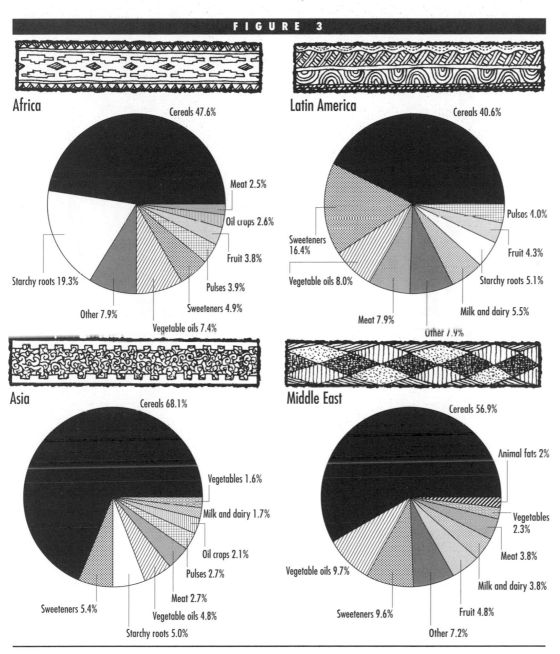

FIGURE 3

Major calorie sources in developing countries

Africa

Cereals 47.6%
Meat 2.5%
Oil crops 2.6%
Fruit 3.8%
Pulses 3.9%
Sweeteners 4.9%
Vegetable oils 7.4%
Other 7.9%
Starchy roots 19.3%

Latin America

Cereals 40.6%
Pulses 4.0%
Fruit 4.3%
Starchy roots 5.1%
Milk and dairy 5.5%
Other 7.9%
Meat 7.9%
Vegetable oils 8.0%
Sweeteners 16.4%

Asia

Cereals 68.1%
Vegetables 1.6%
Milk and dairy 1.7%
Oil crops 2.1%
Pulses 2.7%
Meat 2.7%
Vegetable oils 4.8%
Starchy roots 5.0%
Sweeteners 5.4%

Middle East

Cereals 56.9%
Animal fats 2%
Vegetables 2.3%
Meat 3.8%
Milk and dairy 3.8%
Fruit 4.8%
Other 7.2%
Sweeteners 9.6%
Vegetable oils 9.7%

Changing composition
of diets in
developing countries

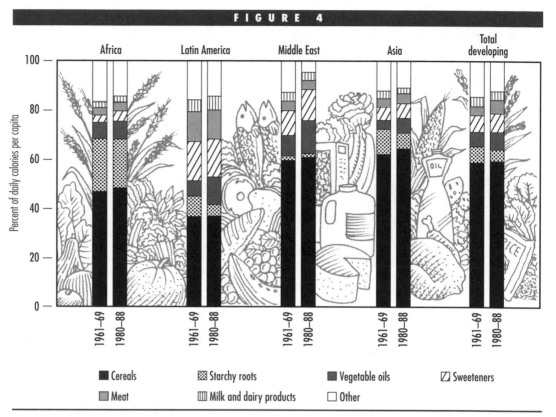

FIGURE 4

Africa   Latin America   Middle East   Asia   Total developing

Percent of daily calories per capita

100

80

60

40

20

0

1961–69 1980–88   1961–69 1980–88   1961–69 1980–88   1961–69 1980–88   1961–69 1980–88

■ Cereals   ▨ Starchy roots   ■ Vegetable oils   ◪ Sweeteners

■ Meat   ▥ Milk and dairy products   ☐ Other

cidental lack of protein and calories. This is most commonly found in infants and young children; it increases the occurrence and severity of infections and ultimately affects growth and mental development. PEM and hunger can also cause low birth weight babies. Low birth weight babies, less than 2,500 grams or 5.5 pounds, are more than twice as likely in developing countries than developed. These children are more susceptible to infection and develop more slowly.

Kwashiorkor and *marasmus* are two severe diseases which stem directly from PEM. Kwashiorkor results from long-term protein deficiency brought on by inadequate energy intake and is characterized by a severe swelling of body tissues, reddish hair, and liver damage. Children between the ages of 1 and 2 are most vulnerable. Marasmus is characterized by severe energy deficiency and weight loss due to the steady wasting of fat and muscle tissues. Both diseases increase the risk and severity of infections by impairing the immune system. For example, a common cold can quickly lead to pneumonia and death.

Measures to reduce the prevalence of PEM include:

- Encouraging breastfeeding (which results in improved immunity, less chronic diarrhea, and increased iron absorption),
- Increasing consumption of cereals and legumes in place of starchy roots,
- Controlling infections and parasitic diseases through improved sanitation and health care,
- Increasing meal frequency of younger children, and
- Encouraging increased consumption of oils and fats.

Oral rehydration therapy (ORT) is an important mechanism for reducing the impact of diarrhea on nutritional status, particularly in young children.

Vitamin A deficiency, which causes blindness in more than half a million children annually,[11] is linked to a lack of green leafy and deep orange vegetables. Deficiency of this essential nutrient also is implicated in increased mortality rates from childhood diseases, particularly measles and diseases of the respiratory tract.

Iodine deficiency occurs most often in the inland areas of Africa and Asia where soils and agricultural crops are naturally low in the mineral.[12] The deficiency leads to an enlargement of the thyroid gland, producing a characteristic swelling of the neck known as *goiter*. Iodine deficiency can also cause an irreversible condition known as *cretinism* in children born to iodine-deficient mothers. Such children suffer both mental and physical retardation.

Iron-deficiency anemia is caused by low iron intake, stemming from a diet low in calories and lacking in variety. A dietary deficiency of vitamin C, which enhances iron absorption from foods, also contributes to anemia. This condition affects an estimated 1.3 billion people worldwide[13] and is a particular problem among pregnant women, who have double the iron requirement of other women. Breastfeeding can significantly increase the iron available for infants. The high fiber content of diets based largely on carbohydrates, particularly those composed mainly of starchy roots, can significantly reduce the body's ability to absorb iron and other essential micronutrients.

Although undernutrition continues to be the overwhelming health problem in developing countries, there is evidence that increased consumption of Western-style diets among some affluent populations in developing countries has led to an increased incidence of diseases related to overnutrition. An FAO study documented a 105-percent increase in the incidence of diet-related noncommunicable diseases in parts of South America during the 1970's.[14] As incomes, food availability, and food variety increase in the developing world, nutrition education will play an important role, particularly in populations that shift to urban areas. Education programs that encourage people in developing countries to avoid the overconsumption of calories, fats, and low-fiber foods may help improve their long-term health status as incomes grow and the demand for such foods increases.

Improving Nutritional Status

Chronic undernourishment is a function of deficient food intake as well as disease, lack of education, inadequate health care, inaccessibility to clean water, and poor sanitation.

Nutrition Policies

Nutrition policies, including education, fortification, and supplementation, can play an important role in improving nutritional status. Nutrition education improves access to and utilization of locally available foods. Small changes in dietary composition—such as the addition of small amounts of wild greens and fruits or greens from locally cultivated starchy roots, such as cassava and sweet potato—can lead to dramatic reductions of vitamin and mineral deficiencies.[15] Encouraging the use and productivity of home gardens can stimulate small-scale production that can provide essential nutrients.

Food fortification and direct supplementation can improve nutritional status, particularly in the case of micronutrient deficiencies.[16] Iodine deficiency has been prevented in industrialized countries for most of this century through the addition of iodine to the salt supply.[17] Iodine fortification is currently taking place in a number of developing countries, including some in Asia where programs are underway to fortify the supply of monosodium glutamate (MSG), a common food ingredient in most Asian households.

Since vitamin A can be stored by the body, periodic direct supplementation through vitamin tablets as infrequently as every 6 months is a relatively simple and inexpensive way to prevent deficiencies. In addition, many foods in developing countries, particularly starchy roots such as cassava and sweet potatoes, are rich in vitamin A. The high fiber content of such foods, however, particularly when used for weaning in infants and young children, significantly reduces the body's ability to absorb and utilize nutrients. Nutrition education which encourages the addition of small amounts of vegetable oils and fats to the diet in such cases can improve vitamin A status.[18]

Prevention of iron deficiency is more problematic, since daily intakes are required. Fortification of bread and cereals may be a useful long-term solution. However, small changes in dietary composition can be important in the short term. For example, increased consumption of small amounts of animal products and vitamin C can improve iron absorption from plant products. Direct supplementation through the distribution of iron tablets, particularly for pregnant women, may also be important in the short term.[19]

Policies targeted toward women that increase their access to agricultural and nutritional information can play an important role in improving the nutritional status of all household members. Since women are the primary care-providers and producers in the household, their role is critical in implementing changes in eating patterns and food choices. Saving women time by making improvements in food processing and providing better and closer sources of water can also be important short-term solutions.

Food Storage, Preservation, and Preparation

Improved storage facilities, better food preservation techniques, and increased development and use of local processing facilities can improve year-round food availability and, hence, nutritional status.

In some developing countries, postharvest losses due to insects, rodents, weather, and microorganisms (including mold), are as high as 5-30 percent for cereals and 15-60 percent for roots, tubers, fruits, and vegetables.[20] Improved postharvest management practices on the farm, in marketing and processing concerns, and in the home can improve nutritional status through increased food availability and lower consumer prices.[21]

Improved food preservation techniques in the home, such as drying, roasting, and fermentation, can significantly improve the nutritional and storage value of food.[22] Encouraging countries to follow international food safety guidelines might lower the risk of infection or disease. This would require improved processing and food inspection procedures.

Domestic Food Production

Most regions of the world have experienced improvements in per capita food production. On average, per capita food output expanded more than 10 percent during the 1980's in developing countries. Asia experienced a small increase in per capita terms, while Latin America held steady. Africa is the exception, as per capita output there declined by about 5 percent during the decade.[23]

Domestic production, however, is not the only determinant of food availability. Stocks and trade also work into the equation. There is not much information on stocks in developing countries, particularly for Africa where much is held on farms, so the focus of attention moves to trade. In many cases, imports have been significant enough to offset a shortfall in domestic production. However, financial constraints often limit imports.

Purchasing Power

Availability of food within a country is often not a problem; it is the lack of purchasing power that is the problem. Incomes in many developing countries are insufficient to purchase a nutritionally adequate diet. In 1990, per capita gross national product (GNP) in the developed countries exceeded $20,000. Incomes in developing countries averaged less than $1,000. The worst cases were South Asia and sub Saharan Africa, where per capita GNP averaged $330 and $340, respectively. Per capita GNP in East Asia exceeded $500, while in Latin America it neared $2,200.[24]

The problem lies not only in the low income levels, but also the low growth rates. According to the World Bank, growth in real per capita gross domestic product (GDP) in developed countries averaged nearly 3 percent per year during the 1980's. On the other hand, GDP growth in developing countries

151

averaged only 1.6 percent per year. The highest growth rate in a developing region—more than 6 percent—was experienced by East Asia. Growth in South Asia measured 3 percent. In sub-Saharan Africa and Latin America, per capita incomes declined 1.2 and 0.4 percent, respectively. Projections for the 1990's do not signal much hope for the poorest regions.

Exports account for a significant portion of developing country income. One of the principal reasons for both the low income levels and the low growth rates is the composition of exports from these countries. Primary commodities—such as oil, coffee, tea, cocoa, and cotton—account for more than half the exports of most African and Latin American countries. World trade in primary commodities is smaller than that in manufactured goods and, in addition, is growing more slowly. During 1980-89, annual growth in the trade of manufactured goods neared 5 percent, while the growth in trade of primary commodities was less than 2 percent. Oil exports, in volume terms, stagnated during the 1980's. Another concern is that the prices received for these commodities were cut in half during the 1980's.[25]

Many developing-country governments have adopted an export-oriented strategy in order to reduce their dependence on primary commodity markets. By encouraging nontraditional exports, this strategy tends to increase export earnings, thus enabling a country to increase commercial imports in case of domestic production shortfalls.

[1]FAO-WHO, Meeting the Nutritional Challenge, Oct. 1990.

[2]Global Hunger: A Look at the Problem and Potential Solutions, Malcolm H. Forbes and Lois J. Merrill, Eds., 1986.

[3]Christian, Janet L. and Janet L. Greger, Nutrition for Living, California, 1988.

[4]FAO-WHO, Meeting the Nutritional Challenge, Oct. 1990.

[5]FAO, Agrostat.

[6]FAO, Agrostat.

[7]Michael C. Latham, Human Nutrition in Tropical Africa, FAO, 1979.

[8]FAO-WHO, Meeting the Nutritional Challenge, Oct. 1990.

[9]Mary Alice Caliendo, "Nutrition and the World Food Crisis," New York, 1979.

[10]Michael C. Latham, "Malnutrition: The Planet's Problem," Human Ecology Forum, vol. 15, no. 3, 1986.

[11]FAO-WHO, Meeting the Nutritional Challenge, Oct. 1990.

[12]Janet L. Christian, and Janet L. Greger, Nutrition for Living, California, 1988.

[13]FAO-WHO, Meeting the Nutritional Challenge, Oct. 1990.

[14]FAO-WHO, Meeting the Nutritional Challenge, Oct. 1990.

[15]Michael C. Latham, Human Nutrition in Tropical Africa, FAO, 1979.

[16]Stuart Gillespie, and John Mason, Nutrition-relevant Actions: Some Experiences from the Eighties and Lessons for the Nineties, United Nations ACC/SCN Nutrition Policy Discussion Paper No. 10, Oct. 1991.

[17]Gillespie and Mason, ibid.

[18]Gillespie and Mason, ibid.

[19]Gillespie and Mason, ibid.

[20]Malcolm C. Bourne, "Proper Care of Food After Harvest," World Food Issues, Ed. Matthew Drosdoff, Cornell University Center for the Analysis of World Food Issues, 1984.

[21]FAO-WHO, Meeting the Nutritional Challenge, Oct. 1990.

[22]FAO-WHO, Meeting the Nutritional Challenge, Oct. 1990.

[23]FAO, Agrostat.

[24]World Bank, World Development Report 1992, Washington, 1992.

[25]World Bank, unpublished report.

Dysfunctional Food Economies: The Case of the Republics of the Former USSR

William Liefert
Agricultural Economist,
Economic Research Service,
USDA, Washington, DC

During the late 1980's and early 1990's, people in the republics of the former Soviet Union (FSU) had increasing difficulty purchasing food. The most common scenes depicting the FSU in Western newspapers were of long lines in front of food stores, with disgruntled customers looking through the windows at barren shelves. One might think that the cause of the apparent food shortages was that there was too little output. The solution would then seem to be to devote more effort and resources to increasing agricultural production.

However, from 1985 to 1990, the first 5 years Gorbachev was in power, output of the most important foodstuffs rose rather than fell, mainly because of more favorable weather. Average annual production of grain and meat in the Soviet Union during these 5 years was about 20 percent higher than in 1981-85. In fact, in 1990 the Soviets had a near-record grain harvest of 235 million metric tons (mmt), before cleaning. The record was 237 mmt in 1978. Also, levels of food consumption were not deficient, even when compared to those of developed countries. During 1987-89, per capita meat consumption in the USSR was about 136 pounds, compared to 147 pounds for Britain and 136 pounds for Finland.

Distribution Breakdown

The main reason the food economy of the FSU became so disrupted is not a reduction in agricultural output, but rather a breakdown in the distribution of the goods produced. When

the Soviet Union broke up in 1991, its system of central supply and distribution ended with it. Also, chronic problems in downstream agricultural activities—transportation, storage, and processing—had a negative effect. These deficiencies, though, were not new; they existed throughout the post-World War II period.

Another important cause of distribution problems was the breakdown of the monetary system—specifically, the weakening of the power of the national currency, the ruble, as effective money. From 1985 to 1991, per capita money income in the former USSR rose about 150 percent. The result was severe inflationary pressure. However, state prices for most consumer goods, including foods, remained controlled at below market-clearing levels. That produced excess demand. The result was all the tell-tale signs of consumer shortages—longer lines for goods, hoarding, barter, and the growth of black markets.

For food, there are two different kinds of shortages: The first is excess consumer demand at existing prices, which can prevail even if supplies are sufficient for adequate diets, and the second is a shortage defined as supply deficiency that might cause real hunger or starvation. In the former Soviet Union, the first type of shortage was more prevalent.

The combination of rising money incomes and controlled prices meant that individuals were earning more rubles than they could possibly spend at existing prices. Because of the large stock of surplus money and inflationary pressure it represented, nobody want-

Apparent food shortages might indicate that there is too little output and a need to increase agricultural production. However, distribution problems were the main reason for disruptions in the food economy in the former Soviet Union.

USDA/92BW1961

Food no longer being immediately bought up by hoarding consumers is available in state stores, as represented in this market.

USDA/92BW1965

ed to sell goods for rubles. The entire economy reverted to crude barter as the dominant mode of exchange, especially at the regional and republic level.

But barter is inefficient, and as a result the flow of inputs and output throughout the economy was severely hindered. Many factories and farms failed to receive the inputs needed to maintain previous production levels. The money surplus also reduced incentives to work, produce, and sell. As a result,

real GNP, industrial output, and agricultural output all fell in 1991.

Because of the distribution problems, some localities failed to receive adequate supplies of certain foods, such as meat, milk, or vegetables. Yet, almost all areas were getting sufficient supplies of bread, the diet staple.

Seeking Market Solutions
In January 1992, the Russian Republic began an ambitious program of economic reform.

The program's longrun goal is to create the institutional conditions for a capitalist market economy. The key policies to do that are privatization of enterprises and private ownership of farmland. The main shortrun goal, though, is to reestablish the ruble as effective money by restoring macroeconomic balance.

As the Russian government recognizes, two policy moves are necessary to restore macroeconomic balance. The first is that the government must prevent the further growth of inflationary pressure. This requires reducing both the budget deficit and the growth of the money supply. The Russian program has promised tough budget, money, and credit policies. These policies, though, reduce the funds available to producing enterprises, and thereby threaten firms with bankruptcy, and workers with the loss of their jobs. In choosing the appropriate fiscal and monetary policies, the government faces a difficult tradeoff, at least in the short term, between reducing inflation and protecting enterprises and employment. This is the most difficult problem facing the entire reform effort.

In addition to stopping the growth, or continued "flow," of consumer purchasing power, the state—in a second policy move—had to mop up the existing "stock" of surplus rubles. The most direct way was to free prices and thereby let them rise to their market-clearing level. On January 2, 1992, Russia began major price liberalization. Prices were completely freed for many producer and consumer goods, including clothing, consumer durables, and most foods, such as meat and sugar. Price controls were kept for fuel, transportation, and some foods, such as bread and milk, but with prices raised significantly. Later in the year, many of the remaining price controls were removed. All the other republics of the former Soviet Union followed Russia's lead to some degree by either freeing or raising prices.

The price liberalization changed the nature of the food problem for FSU consumers. Before, the problem was finding available food to buy in barren state stores, with more rubles in one's pocketbook than one could find goods to spend them on. Now, since food is no longer being immediately bought up by hoarding consumers, it is available in state stores. However, the problem for some people, especially those on less flexible incomes, is that the higher prices are severely stretching their pocketbooks.

The Role of Trade and Food Aid in Meeting Global Food Needs

Gene A. Mathia
Chief, Africa and
Middle East Branch,
Agriculture and Trade
Analysis Division,

Nydia Rivera-Suarez
Agricultural Economist,
Commodity Economics Division,
and

Margaret Missiaen
Agricultural Economist,
Agriculture and Trade
Analysis Division,
Economic Research Service,
Washington, DC

It is well known that many of the world's people do not live where much of the world's food is produced. Industrial countries produce about half of the world's grain, but they have less than a fourth of the world's population (fig. 1). Food supplies are critical to developing countries with chronic food shortages. When they encounter unfavorable growing and harvesting conditions, too often supply crises recur. Furthermore, it is difficult for many countries that are deficient in distribution, storage, and educational resources to meet minimum nutritional standards for the total population.

Other chapters address the many issues related to minimum nutritional standards.

This chapter focuses on ways to help provide minimum supplies of foods for year-round food consumption, especially during chronic and emergency food shortages in developing countries.

Food Supplies

Too little food and a limited variety of foods are serious problems in many developing countries, particularly in Africa. Both problems can usually be traced to resource characteristics, government policies, or both.

Hot desert winds and sparse, infrequent rains, common in much of Africa, contribute to low and variable yields of a few adapted crops. Grain production and consumption are

Hot desert winds and sparse, infrequent rains, common in Africa, contribute to low and variable yields of a few adapted crops.

Photo Courtesy CMS Vickie Graham, USAF

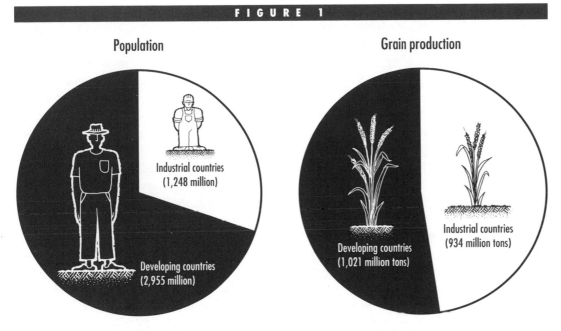

World population and grain production, 1990

FIGURE 1

Population

Industrial countries
(1,248 million)

Developing countries
(2,955 million)

Grain production

Industrial countries
(934 million tons)

Developing countries
(1,021 million tons)

Source: FAO Production Yearbook, 1990.

variable in South Asia, sub-Saharan Africa, and Central America. Only in South Asia is production keeping pace with consumption, but the variability of production remains near the levels in the other two regions and all developing countries (table 1).

In many countries where irrigation possibilities are limited, only a few types of crops are produced. Some staple crops like sorghum and millet are adapted to rain-fed areas, but yields of these drought resistant crops still fluctuate greatly. Both grain sorghum and millet are important crops, but constructing a balanced diet from one or two products is difficult. In the rice- and corn-based countries, land and water resources and weather patterns tend to be more favorable to support a wider variety of production activities and crops.

Options for Providing Foods

In most cases, it is possible to reduce both chronic and transitory food problems, but solutions can be costly and they require planning. Unfortunately, these options are not always cost-effective. An adequate national food supply often can be assured by one or a combination of the following options:

Domestic Production

To enhance domestic production, some of the more common practices are draining, fertilizing, and liming soils; seed improvement; irrigation; variety adaptation; and pest and disease control.

Buffer Stocks

Developing buffer stocks of food in plentiful years for use in lean years is a technique that is frequently used to stabilize domestic supplies. The success of maintaining buffer stocks depends on the capacity of a country to generate surplus production and establish a mechanism to finance the costs of storing stocks.

Historically, developed countries have used this option successfully. The United States, Canada, Australia, and the European Community (EC) are major surplus food suppliers and carry large inventories of agricultural products in reserve to buffer annual production shortfalls and stabilize prices. These reserves are used to service the orders of trading clients. For many cereals, normal pipeline stocks in developed countries represent several months of domestic consumption and trade. In these countries, current and futures prices are sensitive to stocks changes. India and Zimbabwe rely on buffer stocks, but few other developing governments have the resources or the foresight to build substantial

food reserves to stabilize the supplies or prices of storable commodities. Pipeline supplies will often last less than a few weeks.

World prices are responsive to world stocks. When the stocks are drawn down, the results are sharply higher prices and added pressure on foreign reserves for food-deficient countries, especially the debt-laden developing countries. Higher world prices for basic raw commodities of developing countries often help offset the higher costs of imported food. A recent issue of *Africa Recovery*[1] describes how low commodity prices have dealt a severe blow to Africa.

Trade

Trade flow information indicates which countries depend on trade as a food stabilizing option. For example, FAO data indicate that developing countries accounted for about 62 percent of world wheat imports, 76 percent of world rice imports, and 87 percent of world wheat flour imports in 1988. Developing countries accounted for only 36 percent of world corn imports and only 24 percent of total soybean imports. Few developing countries import large amounts of animal feeds. Imports of soybeans are usually in the form of oil for cooking.

Food production does not necessarily correlate with a nation's wealth or the income it generates. It may seem to be highly correlated with income levels because many high-income countries are also food surplus or exporting countries. An exception is Japan, which depends heavily on the food production

In the rice and corn-based countries, land and weather resources and weather patterns tend to be more favorable to support a wider variety of production activities and crops.

Dana Downie/USDA 0785X677-25

capacities of other countries. In 1989, Japan's total merchandise exports were 130 percent of its total imports. For agricultural products, however, its agricultural exports were about 3 percent of its agricultural imports.

Regardless of a country's net trade position, most countries import agricultural products. Even in the United States, one of the world's major agricultural exporting countries, agricultural imports are valued at about 50-60 percent of agricultural exports. Much of the import volume consists of products not commonly produced in the country. Food imports are used to enhance the quality and variety of the American diet throughout the year. Unfortunately, not many of the food-deficient developing countries can afford imported foods for diet enrichment. Imports are used to meet minimum volume requirements of basic foods and tend to be competitive with domestic production.

Trade is a very important vehicle used to balance country and regional demands and supplies, regardless of whether a country's primary concern is quantity or quality of the food supply. While trade can help stabilize the food supply, it may not necessarily help stabilize the domestic price. Agricultural and trade policies are important in determining how domestic prices relate to world prices. Tariff and nontariff barriers and macroeconomic policies are very important determinants of potential trade benefits. Current negotiations at the Uruguay Round of the General Agreement on Tariffs and Trade (GATT) are concerned with getting participating countries to adopt rules and regulations that will make commercial trade a more reliable source of food supplies for all nations and regions.

Other Considerations

Production Variability

World production fluctuates very little when compared with fluctuations of a particular country or region. Grain production variability during 1970-91 was .32 for Sudan compared with .13 for world grain production (see table 1). This means that, on balance, world supplies may be sufficient to adequately supply the needs of the world population while people in one country or region may be facing starvation because of localized production shortfalls or lack of purchasing power to finance imports. For wealthy countries with sufficient international purchasing power, needed supplies can simply be imported from areas fortunate enough to have good yields and surplus production to export. For poor countries without such purchasing power, however, a serious shortfall in production can contribute to malnutrition and starvation. Maintaining a balanced diet becomes the critical issue, usually requiring government intervention and often requests to the international community for help.

TABLE 1		

Variability of production and consumption for selected countries and regions, 1970-91

Country or region	Variability	
	Production	Consumption
	Percent	
World	13	13
Developing countries	17	19
Central America	16	20
Sub-Saharan Africa	14	16
South Asia	18	17
Selected countries		
Sudan	32	19
Ethiopia	16	18
Nigeria	12	14
India	19	17
Mexico	16	20

Urbanization

Increased urbanization in many developing countries also contributes to the problem of distributing available food supplies to all consumers. It is a particular concern in countries with poorly developed marketing networks.

In countries where subsistence agriculture is significant, much of the total food supply is consumed on the farm without entering commercial marketing channels. Marketed surplus is small. Small volumes are stored on the farm, but prices are seldom high enough to

Imported foods usually enter at a seaport or border.

USDA/92CS0527

entice subsistence farmers to sell the surplus with the expectation of buying needed supplies through the marketing system at a future date. During periods of stress, hoarding of available supplies further complicates the availability and distribution of essential foods.

Political Action

Urban consumers often have the political clout to force some type of government action to increase food availability. Government action can take several different forms: (a) forcing farmers to ship available supplies to government-controlled warehouses, (b) grant-ing food subsidies, (c) imposing penalties for hoarding food supplies, and (d) encouraging food imports.

The first three moves are frequently self-defeating. They simply create the psychology of scarcity and increase the rewards for further hoarding, both on the farm and by marketing firms. Consumers also tend to hoard far more food than they need. Thus, this response accentuates the scarcity problem and encourages further hoarding.

The remaining option of importing needed food supplies is not painless. How can a poor country with very limited foreign reserves

163

expect to pay the import bill? Imported foods usually enter at a seaport or border and must be distributed through the marketing system. Prices of imported foods at the point of consumption are often very high because of expensive port and distribution costs. Furthermore, ports in developing countries are often inadequate to handle large shipments of perishable or semiperishable foods. Often imports of commonly consumed foods are not readily available, and substitutes are necessary. For example, white corn is preferred for human consumption in many African countries, but little white corn is available on the world market. Therefore, yellow corn and, in some cases, wheat and rice are substituted. Also at times, wheat and rice are substituted for sorghum and millet.

Limited foreign exchange reduces the import capacity of many developing countries (table 2). Sub-Saharan Africa and Latin America have very high ratios of external debt to exports of goods and services. Sub-Saharan Africa's ratio of external debt to its gross national product is also much higher than in other regions. The lack of foreign exchange is often circumvented by economic assistance programs of higher income countries and by credit and donation programs of food surplus countries. Bilateral and multilateral arrangements, as well as international institutions, can alleviate the foreign exchange problem, but they can do little to solve a country's internal problems concerning distribution or household purchasing power. Some countries have government stores, food subsidy programs, and credit arrangements to help households survive serious food shortages and to lay a base for jump-starting the production process in preparation for the next production cycle.

The Role of Food Aid

Food aid from all donors has been classified into three main categories—program, project, and emergency. International guidelines have been established to outline appropriate donor procedures, sources of financing, and methods of operation for each category.

Program food aid is provided as a grant or on concessional repayment terms. It helps to fill the gap between demand at existing income levels and the supply of food from domestic production and commercial imports. It represents the largest part of food aid supplies to Africa and is provided exclusively on a bilateral government-to-government basis. To the extent that this type of food aid replaces commercial imports, it provides balance-of-payments support, as the foreign exchange that would have been used to pay for those imports is saved. When it is sold in the recipient country, which is usually the case, it provides additional local currency for the government.

Project food aid supports a wide range of development projects for the poor and has improved the nutritional and health status of mothers and preschool children by offering supplemental foods at mother and child health care centers. It has supported education, especially primary schools and training

TABLE 2				

Ratio of total external debt to exports of goods and services and gross national product (GNP) for low- and middle-income countries, 1980 and 1990

Region	External debt as a percentage of:			
	Exports of goods and services *Percent*		Gross National Product (GNP) *Percent*	
	1980	1990	1980	1990
Low- and middle-income countries	127.0	171.3	26.2	40.2
Sub-Saharan Africa	96.8	324.3	28.5	109.4
East Asia & Pacific	88.8	91.1	16.8	26.9
South Asia	162.9	281.5	17.3	30.7
Europe	90.6	125.7	23.8	41.0
Middle East/North Africa	114.9	180.3	31.1	52.6
Latin America and Caribbean	196.8	257.4	35.2	41.6

Source: World Development Indicators, *World Development Report*, 1992, The World Bank, Washington, 1992.

programs; transferred additional income to poor households through food-for-work programs; provided help to poor households during periods of transition to new farming systems; and supported market reform and price stabilization measures by establishing food reserves. Funds saved from governments' budgets have been used to expand or improve development projects or to invest in social services. Some project food is sold to buy local materials, tools, or equipment for the food aid project, generating more employment and higher incomes.

Emergency food aid is a response to unexpected natural disasters, war or civil strife, and shortfalls in food production caused by drought. During the 1980's, emergency food aid took up an increasing proportion of food aid to Africa, primarily for victims of famine. Emergency food aid is provided multilaterally, mostly by the World Food Program (WFP), and also bilaterally. Almost all emergency food aid is free to recipients. A very small amount of food aid for emergency situations is sold within the recipient country to defray some expenses.

International Arrangements for Food Aid Transfers

The international community has agreed on several institutional arrangements aimed at monitoring food aid flows, guaranteeing a minimum availability of food, and ensuring a desirable composition and distribution of this assistance. These arrangements are in the form of general principles or guidelines; they are specific annual quantitative commitments agreed upon by donors as signatories to a convention and an overall food aid target established by the 1974 World Food Conference.

Food aid can be distributed through bilateral arrangements (country-to-country) or multilateral arrangements (through an international organization). Two chief international institutions are involved in bilateral arrangements.

The Food and Agriculture Organization's (FAO) Consultative Subcommittee on Surplus Disposal (CSD) was formed in 1954 and represents the first formal forum for intergovernmental consultations on food aid issues, concerned specifically with the impact of food assistance programs on commercial trade and agricultural production. The CSD follows guidelines specified in the *Principles of Surplus Disposal and Consultative Obligations of Member Countries.*[2] These guidelines also constitute a code of conduct recommended to governments in the provision of food aid. They are designed to ensure that food aid does not displace commercial imports and that domestic production is not discouraged in recipient countries.

The CSD today performs two basic functions, providing a forum through which the donors may notify each other of pending food aid agreements with a particular recipient and offering the opportunity for donors to consult on the manner in which their food assistance is made available.

The other international institution dealing with bilateral food aid is the Food Aid Convention (FAC), part of the International Wheat Trade Agreement. This was the first binding quantitative arrangement agreed upon by donors. This Convention was first signed in 1968 and was renegotiated in 1971, 1980, and 1986. The 1986 FAC was extended through June 1993. Donor countries agreed to provide developing countries with specific amounts of food in the form of grain. The present aggregate minimum annual commitment is about 7.5 million tons in wheat equivalent. This minimum amount comprises a guaranteed floor which should be made available regardless of market conditions. Although individual donors have at times not fulfilled their FAC obligations strictly within the marketing years specified by the Convention, the aggregate minimum donor commitment has always been met and has often been surpassed by a considerable margin.

The World Food Program (WFP), established in 1961, is the main channel for distributing multilateral food aid and one of the major allocators of world cereal aid. The WFP represents the only international forum in which donors and recipients participate jointly in the formulation and implementation of

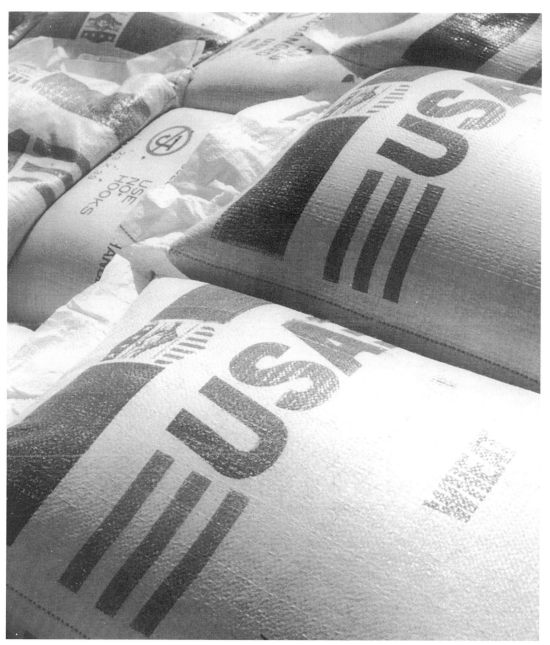

During the 1980's, emergency food aid took up an increasing proportion of food aid to Africa, primarily for victims of famine.

Photo Courtesy CMS Vickie Graham, USAF

food aid policies and programs. Multilateral cereal aid has lately amounted to about 2 million metric tons, or about 25 percent of total cereal aid. Further, the WFP allocates about 30 percent of world vegetable oil aid and more than two-thirds of world skim milk assistance. Pledges to the WFP are voluntary and are made every other year in commodities and cash. The WFP's regular resources are used mainly for development projects. The WFP does not provide program food aid. A separate account was created in 1991 for long-term refugees and displaced persons.

The International Emergency Food Reserve (IEFR) constitutes the only international mechanism specifically intended to respond rapidly to emergency food situations. The IEFR was established in 1975, following a recommendation of the World Food Conference, and is administered by WFP. It has a minimum annual target of 500,000 tons of cereals to be met by voluntary donor contributions. At least one-third of contributions to the Reserve are supposed to be made in the form of cash. However, FAO claims that IEFR's resources have not always proved sufficient or flexible enough to respond to emergencies in recent years.

The creation of the World Food Council (WFC) was one of the principal results of the 1974 World Food Conference. The WFC's most significant food aid policy initiative has been its efforts to urge food donor countries to meet a food aid target of 10 million metric tons per year, a target established by the 1974 World Food Conference. This target was reached for the first time in 1984/85 and has been exceeded, albeit sometimes marginally, in every year since then.

Other major food aid policy concerns monitored by the WFC include diversification of the international food aid basket to include noncereal items, greater specification of the food aid needs of individual recipient countries, wider utilization of food aid purchases from developing country exporters, increased allocation of food aid in the form of grants or on highly concessional terms, and better planning of donor food aid allocation so that longer term, better planned development projects might be undertaken.

The Importance of Food Aid Flows

For 1991/92, available food aid in cereal form is estimated at about 12 million tons, approximately the same level as the year before. During the second half of the 1980's, an average of 12 million tons of commodities was provided as food aid annually. Of this total, more than 90 percent was in the form of cereals, and the remainder was comprised of other food commodities, mostly vegetable oil, dried skim milk, and pulses.

According to the FAO report, *Prospects for Food Aid and Its Role in the 1990's,*[3] cereal food aid shipments to developing countries grew by almost 2 percent annually between 1970 and 1990, while total cereal imports of these countries grew at more than three times this rate. Consequently, the share of food aid as a percentage of total imports has been declining at an annual rate of more than

4 percent. In recent years, food aid amounted to only one-eighth of developing countries' cereal imports, as compared to one-fourth in the early 1970's. However, for a large number of countries food aid remains a very important source of imported supplies.

The same report showed that for over 40 recipient countries, cereal food aid represents over 40 percent of total cereal imports. In sub-Saharan Africa, in particular, more than 40 percent of the imported cereals are in the form of food aid, and this dependence on food aid has been growing by over 5 percent annually.

Major Donors of Food Aid

The major donors of cereal food aid continue to be the United States, the European Community (EC), Canada, Japan, and Australia. The United States is estimated to have provided about 62 percent of total cereal food aid in 1990/91, followed distantly by the EC with 18 percent, Canada with 12 percent, and Japan and Australia with 4 and 3 percent, respectively.

Although cereals dominate total food aid (more than 90 percent of volume during the last 3 years), contributions of dairy products and other noncereal foods have been growing much faster. The United States and the EC account for more than 90 percent of total non-cereal aid shipments.

The United States has been a strong supporter of multilateral food aid provided through the United Nations system and is the largest donor of food aid. The United States has consistently exceeded its annual 4.5-million-ton pledge to the FAC. Most U.S. food aid that is provided multilaterally goes through WFP. The United States was a major force in the creation of WFP in 1961, providing over half of the total voluntary pledges made for its first 3-year experiment period (1963-65). Since then, it has remained the largest single donor. It was also an early contributor to the United Nations Relief and Rehabilitation Administration (UNRRA) and has provided food aid through the United Nations Children's Fund (UNICEF) and the United Nations High Commissioner for Refugees (UNHCR).

In recent years, U.S. commodity pledges to WFP have consisted of about 20 food items, the bulk of which have been in cereals and blended foods. The United States is the only supplier to WFP of bulgur wheat, blended foods, and soy-fortified products. The proportion of total pledges provided by the United States to WFP's regular program has fallen as other donors have increased their contributions. The United States has also made contributions to the IEFR every year since 1978. Those contributions have ranged from $25 million to $286 million a year, including contributions to protracted refugee and displaced person operations. U.S. contributions to the IEFR are not made in advance, but must be in response to individual requests for emergency aid.

The EC is the second largest food aid donor after the United States, and all of its food aid is provided as grants. The FAO estimates that the EC will deliver about 2 million tons of cereal food aid in 1991/92, the same as the previous year. Most of the EC cereal food aid is channeled bilaterally. However, the

WFP is the main multilateral channel distributing the balance. Noncereal food aid from the EC comprises mostly milk powder and butter oil.

Canada has been providing food aid since the early 1950's, and now ranks third behind the United States and the EC in terms of total volume of aid supplied. Nearly half of Canada's 1991/92 food aid budget was disbursed through multilateral channels such as the WFP and IEFR. The balance was disbursed bilaterally, either as government-to-government assistance or through Canadian nongovernmental organizations. Canada's total cereal food aid remains at near 1.3 million tons in 1991/92.

Traditionally, Canadian food aid goes primarily to Asian countries, followed by Africa and Latin America. Wheat and wheat flour represented three-fourths of total shipments in 1990/91. Other commodities included vegetable oil, pulse, corn, skim milk powder, and fish. All Canadian assistance is given as grants.

The FAO estimates Japanese cereal aid shipments in 1991/92 to be about 450,000 tons, the same level as the previous year. Most Japanese aid is provided bilaterally. Traditionally, Japan buys all the commodities it provides as food aid from other countries. It continues to buy its wheat donations from the Unites States, its rice from Asian countries, and coarse grains from Zimbabwe, primarily for distribution to Africa. In 1990, Japan became one of the world's largest donors of foreign aid when it provided about $9 billion in Official Development Aid (ODA).

Australia is one of the top five providers of food aid to developing countries, and all of its food aid is in the form of grants. Australia purchases its food aid commercially, mostly from Australian suppliers. Traditionally, grains (mostly wheat and rice) make up the largest component of Australian food aid shipments. The FAO estimates Australian cereal food aid shipments at about 350,000 tons in 1991/92, exceeding its 1990/91 shipments by 50,000 tons.

Need for Food Aid

Even the most optimistic assumptions about food production and the most pessimistic assumptions about food consumption in third world countries indicate that food aid imports must grow considerably during the 1990's. The need for more food aid is a result of an increased number of malnourished people, growing food imports, worsening balance of payments, and high levels of debt servicing in many developing countries. The FAO study *World Agriculture Toward 2000*[4] emphasized that even if production accelerated, the high rate of population growth, especially in Africa, would require an increase in cereal imports to maintain nutritional status at 1980 levels.

However, while the demand for food aid seems likely to increase, the actual level of food aid flows will depend on many other factors. Food aid flows have varied considerably over time and are influenced by the level of inventories in donor countries, world prices of food aid commodities, food gaps in recipient countries, and the development assistance objectives and institutional commitments of donors.

Recent estimates of food aid requirements published by the National Research Council in its *Food Aid Projections for the Decade of the 1990's*[5] study suggest that food aid will have to double present levels of about 10 million metric tons per year in order to meet projected needs. Furthermore, the study pointed out that much more is needed if minimum nutritional requirements are to be met.

According to the same study, Africa continues to be the region of most concern for food aid, and also the region of greatest uncertainty because of continuing conflict, cycles of drought and floods, and low economic growth combined with high population growth. However, in the longer run, the food security situation in Asia might deteriorate if population growth exceeds production gains.

Conclusions

The availability and stability of food supplies are important concerns of developing countries. Several options have been discussed which offer potential solutions to both chronic and transitory food shortages. Trade is one option available to developing countries. Before trade can be a feasible solution, however, a country must resolve its foreign exchange problems and overcome barriers preventing the free trade of commodities.

Donor countries can use their production capacity to help ease the tragedy of hunger and malnutrition in Third World countries. Food aid moves through bilateral and multilateral channels to help meet food needs. However, the need for more food aid remains. It appears that food aid will be needed on an increasingly larger scale. Most major donors still are committed to the principle of food aid as a vehicle to mitigate hunger and improve food security in recipient countries.

---

[1]Roy Laishley, "Commodity Prices Deal Blow to Africa," *Africa Recovery*, vol. 6, no. 1, April, New York, 1992.
[2]FAO, *Principles of Surplus Disposal and Consultative Obligations of Member Nations*, Rome, 1980.
[3]FAO, *Prospects for Food Aid and its Role in the 1990's*, Rome, April 1991.
[4]FAO, *World Agriculture Toward 2000*, Rome, 1981.
[5]National Research Council, *Food Aid Projections for the Decade of the 1990's*, Washington, Oct. 1988.

Prospects for Improving the Global Food Support System

Cheryl Christensen
International Programs Coordinator,
Economic Research Service,
Dana Dalrymple
Agricultural Economist,
Office of International
Cooperation and Development,
Carole Levin
International Affairs Specialist,
Office of International
Cooperation and Development,
and
Roberta van Heaften
Agricultural Economist,
Office of International
Cooperation and Development,
all with USDA in
Washington, DC

This chapter explores the frontier in two areas that are key to the operation of the global food support system:

1. Early warning systems, which enable us to identify and respond to food crises, and
2. International agricultural research, which generates production and marketing technologies to reduce the likelihood of malnutrition and food crises.

In both areas, our current knowledge provides the opportunity to significantly improve the operation of the global food support system. The global food support system includes the network of commercial trade and food aid ties among nations, as well as the operations of international organizations and private voluntary organizations that aim to improve food security and agricultural development.

This global food support system has fallen short of the goal set for it by Henry Kissinger at the World Food Conference in 1974—that within a decade, no child should go to bed hungry.

While some progress has been made, it is increasingly clear that international actions alone cannot achieve this goal. Broad-based, sustainable economic growth is the only feasible and cost-effective way to lift most people out of poverty and malnutrition.

Many of the catalysts for such economic development depend primarily upon developing countries—their economic and trade policies, their commitment to agricultural development and the operation of efficient domestic food markets, and their choices about whether or how to meet the special nutritional needs of particular groups.

In other areas, joint national and international action is critical. The global food support system plays a vital role in mobilizing and distributing assistance to countries facing famine or other food emergencies. Effective international markets increase food availability for many developing countries. Indeed, one of the principal findings of a decade of research is that self-reliance, based on effective market and trade relations, is far superior to a strategy aimed at achieving national food self-sufficiency.

The goal of food self-reliance is that each developing country should progress to the point where domestic production and export earnings are sufficient to end food shortages and provide enough economic surplus to support transfers to individuals and households unable to provide for themselves. The goal of food self-sufficiency is to cover the nation's consumption of basic foodstuffs from domestic production.[1]

International research has made important contributions to increasing food supplies, as well as providing new insights that can improve nutrition and the operation of nutrition intervention programs.[2]

Early Warning and Food Emergencies

USDA, the U.S. Agency for International Development (USAID), and the United Nations Food and Agricultural Organization (FAO) have each developed systems to monitor crop conditions and food emergencies throughout the world. USDA's Foreign Agri-

FAS crop analyst Paulette Sandene (left) and agronomist Mark Lindeman use state-of-the-art computer equipment to monitor global crop conditions.

Ken Hammond/USDA 93BW0182-6

cultural Service (FAS) operates a state-of-the-art system for monitoring global crop conditions. The countries that are currently monitoring priorities are the United States, Mexico, Brazil, Paraguay, Argentina, Eastern Europe, the major agricultural areas of the former Soviet Union, Pakistan, India, Bangladesh, China, Australia, the Middle East, North Africa, Sudan, Ethiopia, and Southern Africa. The commodities covered include wheat, coarse grains, rice, oilseeds, and cotton.

The USDA system uses satellite imagery, weather data, and knowledge of the countries' production patterns, soils, and geography to provide regular crop assessments and production estimates.

The USDA system uses remote sensing data from both the Landsat and Metsat satellites. Landsat imagery is purchased from the Earth Observation Satellite Company and Metsat imagery is provided by the National Oceanographic and Atmospheric Administration (NOAA) of the U.S. Department of Commerce. Imagery is received and analyzed daily. Crop analysts use imagery analysis techniques to extract information on current crop conditions from remote sensing data. They compare current patterns with an historical series of Vegetative Index Numbers (VIN) that measure the "greenness" of previous harvests during comparable periods of the growth cycle. Analysts can thus compare current crop conditions with those of previous years. This comparison, coupled with techniques and models for obtaining estimates of yield, allows them to make estimates of commodity production. These are updated weekly during critical growing periods. FAS agricultural attaches and counselors in key countries provide on-the-ground information to complement the technology-based assessments.

USDA's estimates are used primarily to monitor and forecast conditions in world commodity markets. They also provide early warning of food emergencies, as well as quantitative estimates of the magnitude of the production shortfall. Timely information allows commercial imports and food aid to begin flowing in time to prevent widespread hunger and famine.

USAID System
USAID also maintains a monitoring system—the Famine Early Warning System (or FEWS). FEWS is more narrowly focused on African countries that have experienced severe food emergencies. It initially focused on Burkina Faso, Chad, Ethiopia, Mali, Mauritania, Niger, and Sudan, and is currently being expanded to include southern Africa. The FEWS mandate is somewhat broader than crop assessment, however. It also provides information on nonproduction problems that could lead to famine conditions or complicate relief efforts. FEWS is also responsible for disseminating this information to national and USAID decisionmakers and donors soon enough to allow them to act to prevent large-scale famine.

FEWS does not maintain an independent remote sensing capacity. It obtains agroclimat-

Crop analysts use imagery to extract information on current crop conditions.

Ken Hammond/USDA 93BW0183-28

ic data through cooperation with African regional agroclimatic sensing centers, international organizations (such as FAO) and U.S. Government departments (such as USDA and the Department of Commerce). Field representatives stationed in a particular country provide current assessments of conditions and work with local officials to assemble and interpret information. The Washington office publishes an assessment of each country's food system three times a year, and supplements this with bulletins charting crop development.

FAO System

FAO also maintains an early warning system—the Global Information and Early Warning System (GIEWS). GIEWS combines current crop information, drawn both from field representatives and remote sensing, with its food balance database to identify emerging food emergencies and conditions which could affect the food security of vulnerable groups.[3] It produces monthly summaries of regional crop conditions, and highlights areas with emergency needs. Followup assessment missions are used to determine how much external food assistance is required, locate the areas of greatest need, and assess the logistical capacity to handle food assistance.

Improved Predictions Result

These crop assessment and monitoring capabilities have significantly improved the international food support system. The international community has had more timely and reliable information on food emergencies in the 1980's—most of them in Africa. Early estimates of the impact of the severe drought in Southern Africa, combined with information on shipping and logistics constraints, have allowed countries in the region and food aid donors to organize the importation and delivery of an unprecedented 10.1 million tons of food to the region.

Improvements in early warning systems are possible in two major areas: First, continued improvements in satellite surveillance, coupled with the development of larger, more integrated databases, will provide better analyses of the magnitude and potential impact of food shortages. Work in these areas is ongoing in USDA and FAO. Second, food security research during the last decade has shown that monitoring local market conditions, as well as local crop conditions, is critical to improving effective responses to food emergencies. USDA, USAID, and FAO are all taking steps to integrate such information into their early warning systems.

The major failings of the global food support systems occur when food emergencies are embedded in ongoing conflicts. The difficulties in providing humanitarian assistance to people caught in domestic or international conflicts have been abundantly demonstrated in Somalia, Ethiopia, Sudan, Mozambique, Angola, and Liberia. Recent experiences in Bosnia and Armenia suggest that these problems exist in European ethnic conflicts as well.

International Agricultural Research

Improved technology is a key ingredient in expanding food production. The principal way to improve technology is through research. In developed countries, research is carried out in both the public and private sectors. In less developed countries, research is conducted principally in the public sector, mainly by national agricultural research programs which are usually connected with ministries of agriculture. However, colleges of agriculture and private firms are becoming increasingly involved.

All of these groups have greatly benefited from the work of a relatively small number of international agricultural research centers (IARCs) which have been developed over the past 30 years. Most of the IARCs are members of the Consultative Group on International Agricultural Research (CGIAR), which is cosponsored by the World Bank, FAO, and the United Nations Development Program. The CGIAR is composed of approximately 40 donors. The United States is a major donor through USAID. (See table 1.) These centers have generated improved forms of technology that are tailored for use at the local level by the national agricultural research programs.

FAS crop analysts Paulette Sandene (left) and Ron White review imagery for current crop conditions.

Ken Hammond/USDA 93BW0183-7

The best known product of the international agricultural research system has been widely known as the "Green Revolution," the introduction of high-yielding varieties of wheat and rice beginning in the 1960's. Initially, the wheat varieties were developed by CIMMYT, the rice varieties by IRRI. Both crops are extensively grown under irrigation in developing countries and the high-yielding varieties proved to be widely adaptable in these regions. Now most of the wheat and rice varieties grown under irrigation in developing nations incorporate CIMMYT, IRRI, or other IARC varieties in their ancestry.

Today many developing countries need low-cost technologies which can cope with disease outbreaks and pest infestations that damage crops both in the field and in storage. Low-cost, environment-preserving technologies lower farmers' adoption costs and provide alternatives to inappropriately using marginal land for food production.

The international centers have increasingly attempted to provide technologies more

Although the centers are primarily oriented to providing technologies for developing nations, some of their work is also of value to developed nations, and they form bridges among regions.

The major challenge in developing nations is to provide an adequate supply of food for the large low-income sector. Primary emphasis in the CGIAR system is on expanding the caloric supply, since a mixed diet that contains adequate calories generally contains an adequate supply of protein.

Expanding food production benefits both producers and consumers. Producer benefits largely flow to early adopters of new technologies. In contrast, all consumers benefit through expanded food supplies and the resulting lower prices. Lower prices are particularly important in low-income countries, where the poorest 20 percent of the population spend 60 percent or more of their income on food and are still unable to purchase a nutritionally adequate diet. In one calculation, a reduction in prices in developing nations led to an increase in real income for poor households twice that for rich households.[4] There are also other, more indirect, economic benefits from the improved technologies. Both direct and indirect contributions lay the base for broader economic development—generally leading to improved nutrition.

suited to the countries' physical and economic environment. For example, CIAT has successfully bred resistance to Mexican bean beetle into beans, and these genes now provide a nonchemical means to control this pest—which devours 25 percent of the beans stored in Africa and 15 percent in Latin America. It is interesting to note that this success is the result of the foresight of a USDA scientist, Dr. H.S. Gentry, who 20 years ago saved a handful of seed from a then useless wild bean plant. The seeds made their way to CIAT's bean seed bank and were later crossed with modern varieties.

IITA's research has improved disease resistance in bananas and plantains, crops that provide 400 million people in the tropics with 80 percent of their carbohydrates. An overriding worldwide constraint to production is black sigatoka disease. It has been difficult to breed resistance to this disease into domesticated bananas and plantains because they reproduce asexually by suckers. IITA scientists made an important and rapid breeding breakthrough by using IITA's collection of 400 wild banana and plantain varieties from around the world to identify resistant varieties that could be propagated sexually. Biotechnologies were used to produce hybrid, black sigatoka-resistant plants in one-third the normal time that yield twice the normal amount of fruit.

CIP has just recently met its goal of reduced insecticide use in potatoes with the development of the "hairy potato." The newly developed hairy potato has tiny, sticky hairs on its leaves and stems that trap aphids, bee-

TABLE 1

Primary International Agricultural Research Centers (IARC)

Consultative Group on International Agricultural Research (CGIAR)

CIAT	International Center for Tropical Agriculture - Cali, Colombia
CIFOR	Center for International Forestry Research - Bogor, Indonesia
CIMMYT	International Maize and Wheat Improvement Center - near Mexico City, Mexico
CIP	International Potato Center - Lima, Peru
IBPGR	International Board for Plant Genetic Resources - Rome, Italy
ICARDA	International Center for Agricultural Research in the Dry Areas - Aleppo, Syria
ICLARM	International Center for Living Aquatic Resources Management - Manila, Philippines
ICRAF	International Center for Research in Agroforestry - Nairobi, Kenya
ICRISAT	International Crops Research Institute for the Semi-Arid Tropics - near Hyderabad, India
IFPRI	International Food Policy Research Institute - Washington, DC
IIMI	International Irrigation Management Institute - Colombo, Sri Lanka
IITA	International Institute of Tropical Agriculture - Ibadan, Nigeria
ILCA	International Livestock Center for Africa - Addis Ababa, Ethiopia
ILRAD	International Laboratory for Research on Animal Diseases - Nairobi, Kenya
INIBAP	The International Network for the Improvement of Banana and Plantain - Montpellier, France
IRRI	International Rice Research Institute - near Manila, Philippines
ISNAR	International Service for National Agricultural Research - The Hague, Netherlands
WARDA	West Africa Rice Development Association - Bouake, Côte d'Ivoire

Other

AVRDC	Asian Vegetable Research and Development Center - Taipei, Taiwan
IBSRAM	International Board for Soil Research and Management - Bangkok, Thailand
ICIPE	International Center for Insect Physiology and Ecology - Nairobi, Kenya
IFDC	International Fertilizer Development Center - Muscle Shoals, Alabama

tles, and other insect pests like flypaper. By reducing the need for insecticides—more pesticides are applied to potatoes than to any other food crop—the hairy potato will lower production costs and alleviate environmental problems. These effects will encourage production of this nutritious crop, which has tremendous potential for keeping developing nations better fed.

ICRAF is working with farmers in several African countries to intercrop their corn fields with rows of leguminous trees. Use of these nitrogen-fixing trees has increased corn yields by 50 percent and makes the growing of corn a more sustainable and beneficial enterprise. The tree's leafy branches, when cut and placed in between the corn, provide the crop with "green manure" fertilizer. The leaves can also be used as a high-protein feed for livestock. The branches make good fuel for cooking. This system has great promise not only in Africa but also for developing nations in other regions. Other agroforestry systems are being developed which stabilize areas prone to desertification and permit crop cultivation without destroying the vegetation needed to prevent delicate tropical soils from degradation and erosion.

New Foods Developed

The international agricultural research system has also been instrumental in introducing new foods that have improved diets of people in poor countries. AVRDC helped restore food supplies to cyclone-stricken Bangladesh—where farmers lost both their crops and valuable seed stores—by introducing a promising new leafy green vegetable, kangkong. Kangkong is hardy, fast-growing, and disease-tolerant, and it can be raised throughout the year. It is rich in vitamins and minerals that are chronically deficient in Bangladesh diets and can also be used as a feed supplement for cattle and poultry. Other advantages include a desirable flavor and texture and ease of propagation by cuttings. The result has been quick and widespread adoption. Kangkong represented up to 50 percent of the volume of vegetables available in local markets, benefiting both farmers and consumers.

ICLARM helped displaced Indonesian families reclaim their lives through aquaculture. In 1985, the Indonesian government dammed a river in Java to provide electricity to the island. Over 12,000 acres of productive farmland were flooded and 44,000 families displaced. ICLARM, in collaboration with several public Indonesian institutions, took advantage of the newly created water reservoirs to develop a carp and tilapia fish industry that, 5 years later, is thriving.

Research is also underway in many centers to develop improved crop varieties for rainfed areas. For example, ICARDA scientists have been working to breed a better chickpea by crossing modern varieties with their "wild" ancestors. These wild varieties have the cold- and drought-resistant qualities that would enable cultivation of chickpeas during the Mediterranean winter. An added winter crop would increase yields by 70 percent and enable Middle Eastern countries to more nearly meet their domestic needs for this nutritious crop.

Effects of Research on Nutrition

What have these efforts, and associated developments in agriculture, accomplished on a broader level? One study of the effect of modern varieties a few years ago concluded that by moderating food prices they "have been the chief factor in improving the nutrition of the poor in the developing world."[5]

Agricultural research is one of the major forces for transforming the world food support system. With the widespread adoption of more market-oriented policies in many developing countries, there is a more favorable economic climate for the adoption of new food production and marketing technologies. Linking research with the forces released by policy reform and privatization can create a new and powerful force for improving both nutrition and economic development over the next decade.

---

[1]See, for example, M. Rukuni, G. Mudimu, and T.S. Jayne, *Food Security in the SADCC Region*, Proceedings of the Fifth Annual Conference on Food Security Research in Southern Africa, Oct. 16-18, 1989; and Joachim von Braun and Eileen Kennedy, *Commercialization of Subsistence Agriculture: Income and Nutritional Effects in Developing Countries*, International Food Policy Research Institute.

[2]See Beatrice Lorge Rogers, "Food, Health, Nutrition and Development," theme paper prepared for the International Conference on Nutrition, 1992.

[3]FAO/WHO, International Conference on Nutrition, *Policies and Programs To Improve Nutrition*, paragraph 24.

[4]Jock Anderson, Robert Herdt, and Grant Scobie, *Science and Food: The CGIAR and Its Partners*, The World Bank, Washington, DC, 1988, p. 83.

[5]Anderson, Herdt, and Scobie, p. 84.

International Conference on Nutrition

Neil Gallagher
International Relations Advisor,
Office of International
Cooperation and Development,
USDA, Washington, DC

The United States joined 158 other nations and the European Community in Rome in December 1992 for the International Conference on Nutrition (ICN). The meeting was sponsored by the Food and Agriculture Organization (FAO) and World Health Organization (WHO), with other United Nations (UN) agencies also contributing.

Pope John Paul II opened the conference with a strong endorsement of UN intervention in countries whenever people are suffering from widespread hunger and malnutrition.

The ICN adopted a Global Declaration and Plan of Action, including a pledge to reduce substantially, within this decade, starvation and widespread hunger and undernutrition, as well as a request that the United Nations declare a Decade on Food and Nutrition to follow up the recommendations of the ICN.

On other issues of particular interest to the United States, the meeting called for international harmonization of nutrition labeling of processed foods. It noted the high level of consumption of fats and "complex carbohydrates" in many nations, but declined to endorse global dietary guidelines or specific targets for daily consumption of nutrients such as fats and sugars. It gave a strong endorsement to FAO's International Code of Conduct on Pesticides, calling on nations to legislate compliance or otherwise provide for its implementation, where appropriate. This Code of Conduct calls for comprehensive labeling of agricultural chemicals so developing country users in particular are properly informed and can deal with health and food safety issues.

At the meeting, USDA announced donations of $82 million in food aid through the World Food Programme for use in African emergencies and in food-for-work and other development projects. A new U.S. Agency for International Development initiative to curb micronutrient deficiency diseases, funded at $50 million, was also announced

As expected, much of the discussion focused on international issues related to nutrition, especially on the serious problems of developing nations—where nearly 800 million people suffer from chronic hunger and malnutrition. There was considerable discussion on ways to strengthen the nutritional impact of food aid, micronutrient deficiencies, sustainable agriculture, food safety and quality, and agricultural trade. Nutrition research was not treated as a separate element, but there were calls for additional assistance in this area to developing nations and for improved cooperation among developed countries in sharing information on ongoing nutrition research.

As a followup to the conference, the United States will be expected to draw up a National Plan of Action for Nutrition no later than the end of 1994. USDA, the U.S. Department of Health and Human Services, and interested representatives from private voluntary, consumer, and food industry groups will develop a National Plan of Action, working with the Department of State and the Agency for International Development on aspects relating to international activities.

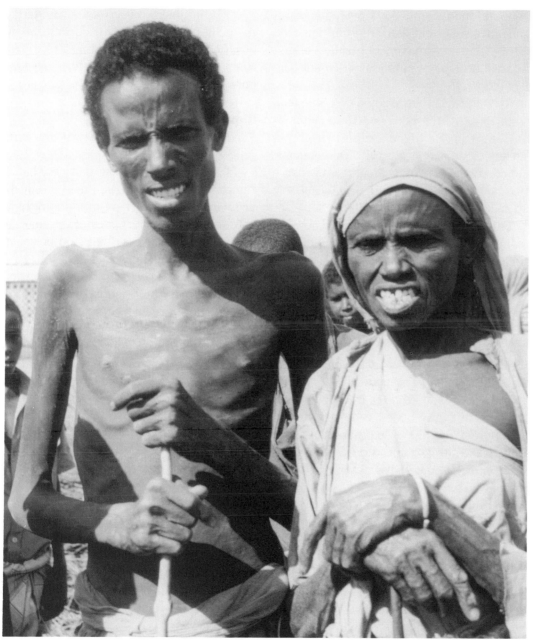

Pope John Paul II opened the International Conference on Nutrition in December 1992 with a strong endorsement of UN intervention in countries whenever people are suffering from widespread hunger and malnutrition.

Photo courtesy of Department of Defense/92BW2004

Appendix I
Safe Food Handling for Optimum Nutrition

Susan D. Conley
Manager,
Meat and Poultry Hotline,
FSIS, USDA,
Washington, DC,
Elizabeth L. Andress
National Program Leader,
for Food Science,
Home Economics, and
Human Nutrition,
Extension Service, USDA,
Washington, DC,
and
Mark L. Tamplin
Associate Professor
of Food Safety,
Department of
Home Economics,
Institute of Food and
Agricultural Sciences,
University of Florida,
Gainesville

Good nutrition and food safety are important consumer issues of the 1990's. Nutrition, food safety, and health are integrally related because no food is nutritious if it's not handled properly.

Overall, Americans enjoy a very safe food supply. USDA, the Food and Drug Administration, the Environmental Protection Agency, State and local Health Departments, and others are all working together to ensure that food is safe, wholesome, and accurately labeled.

Then why should consumers be concerned about food safety? Because even though food is inspected, it can contain bacteria that can cause illness if it is not handled properly. Meat, poultry, fish, eggs, fruits, and vegetables may contain bacteria. These bacteria are present throughout our environment.

At the right temperature, in just a few hours, small amounts of bacteria that you can't see, smell, or taste can multiply to dangerous levels on food and cause foodborne illness, sometimes called food poisoning. Common symptoms of many foodborne illnesses are flu-like and include diarrhea, which prevents the body's absorption of the nutrients in food.

Everyone in the food chain plays a role in food safety. Most of us eat foods grown and packaged many miles away, yet safe handling of food is as critical in the home as it is in a processing plant, retail store, or restaurant. The food preparer—in homes, restaurants, and institutions—has the final control over the safety of the food on the family table.

The consumer's role in food safety starts at the point of purchase and ends with the disposal of leftovers. By following these basic rules and handling food safely, most foodborne illness can be prevented.

Shopping
Food safety in the home actually starts at the grocery store.

Plan your purchases so that perishables (meat, poultry, seafood, and dairy products) are selected last. These foods should be refrigerated within 2 hours of purchase (1 hour in hot weather) so that food poisoning bacteria do not multiply.

Bag meat and poultry products to prevent juices from dripping onto other foods and keep them separated from other foods, especially foods that will not be cooked such as fruits and vegetables.

Buy packaged precooked foods only if packaging is sound, and buy products labeled "keep refrigerated" only if they are stored in a refrigerated case.

Storing Food
Proper storage of food prolongs its shelf-life and preserves nutrients as well as safety. Foods stored too long gradually spoil and also will lose nutritional value.

Make sure your refrigerator is kept clean and maintains a temperature no higher than 40°F.

Your frozen foods will maintain top flavor and nutritional value if the freezer is kept at 0°F or below.

Be sure to keep raw meat and poultry separate from other foods, especially those that will be eaten without further cooking. Poultry and ground meat will keep 1-2 days in the refrigerator; other meat items, 3-4 days.

Canned goods and other shelf-stable items should be stored in a cool, dry place. The temperature should stay above freezing and below 85°F.

Preparing Food

Cleanliness is the first critical step in safe food preparation. Wash hands thoroughly with soap and water before handling food. Wash hands, utensils, cutting boards, and work areas after handling raw products.

Frozen foods should never be thawed at room temperature. Instead, thaw them safely in the refrigerator. Thaw in the microwave only immediately before cooking.

It is essential that raw products of animal origin be cooked to an internal temperature of 160°F (180°F for poultry). Use a meat thermometer to check the temperature of meat and poultry. To check visually, juices should run clear and meat should not be pink.

Do not partially cook food. Have a constant heat source, and don't set the oven temperature under 325°F for cooking meat, poultry, seafood, or dairy-based foods. Microwave food in a covered dish and turn the dish frequently.

Serving Food

Food safety errors can be made during the serving and handling of cooked food.

When serving foods be sure to wash hands

COOKING TEMPERATURES

Product	Fahrenheit
Eggs & Egg Dishes	
Eggs	Cook until yolk and white are firm
Egg dishes	160
Ground Meat & Meat Mixtures	
Turkey, chicken	170
Veal, beef, lamb, pork	160
Fresh Beef	
Rare (some bacterial risk)	140
Medium	160
Well Done	170
Fresh Veal	
Medium	160
Well Done	170
Fresh Lamb	
Medium	160
Well Done	170
Fresh Pork	
Medium	160
Well Done	170
Poultry	
Chicken, whole	180
Turkey, whole	180
Poultry breast, roasts	170
Poultry thighs, wings	Cook until juices run clear
Stuffing (cooked alone or in bird)	165
Duck & Goose	180
Ham	
Fresh (raw)	160
Pre-cooked (to reheat)	140

Cleanliness is the first critical step in safe food preparation.

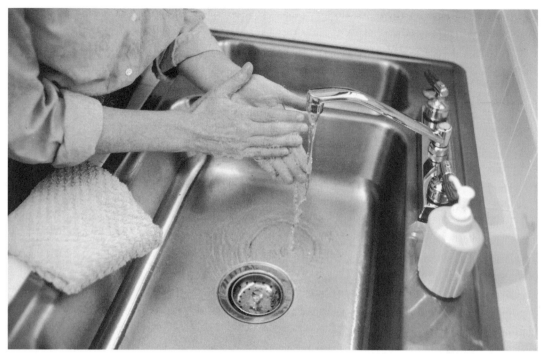

Bob Nichols/USDA 93BW1982

thoroughly with hot soapy water. Serve cooked products on clean plates and with clean utensils.

Foods should never sit at room temperature longer than 2 hours, 1 hour in hot weather. During serving, hot foods should be held above 140°F and cold foods should be kept cold.

Leftovers

When handling leftovers, cleanliness and temperature control are critical.

Wash hands before handling leftovers and use clean utensils and surfaces.

Refrigerate or freeze cooked leftovers in small, covered shallow containers within 2 hours after cooking. Leave airspace around containers in the refrigerator to ensure rapid, even cooling.

When reheating leftovers, cover and reheat thoroughly. Sauces, soups, and gravies should be heated to a rolling boil; all other products should be heated to 165°F.

Food spoilage bacteria will grow in the refrigerator, so discard any outdated foods. Most foods will remain safe in the refrigerator for about 4 days, but use highly perishable foods such as stuffing or gravy within 1-2 days.

When in doubt, throw it out!

Kids, for Safe Microwaving:

- Read the package instructions carefully.
- Use only microwave-safe cookware.
- Turn food in the microwave during cooking.
- Use potholders to take items from the oven.
- Take covers off food or open packages away from the face.

Special tips for favorite foods:

Hotdogs: Pierce the skin before cooking.

Jelly donuts: Break open before eating. Let the jelly cool.

Popcorn: Let the bag sit for a minute or so. Hold bag away from face to open.

Food Safety for Children

Spend some time in a roomful of kids—no matter what their ages—and you're likely to emerge exhausted. Yet, food safety experts classify children as a group at high risk for foodborne illness! Safe food handling practices can prevent food poisoning among children.

Infants

Infants are at high risk for foodborne illness: even a small amount of food poisoning bacteria can cause a serious illness in an infant.

Caregivers must keep scrupulously clean all items used in feeding an infant.

Frequent handwashing is essential. Cases of foodborne illness in infants have been linked to the lack of handwashing by caregivers after handling raw meat or poultry or changing diapers.

Never leave baby food or formula out for more than 2 hours. Discard any unused milk left in a bottle.

Do not feed a baby food directly from a jar—bacteria from baby's mouth may contaminate the food left in the jar.

Expressed breast milk can be stored in the refrigerator for 5 days, formula for 2 days, and whole milk for 5 days. Leftover homemade baby foods may be safely refrigerated for 1 to 2 days. Strained fruits and vegetables in jars will keep 2 to 3 days, meats and eggs one day, meat and vegetable combinations 1 to 2 days.

Toddlers

Toddlers are "grown up" enough to be eating table foods and drinking from a cup. Cleanliness in still essential. Remember to clean off those little hands!

Finger foods are popular with toddlers, but remember that meat and dairy products require refrigeration and should never be left at room temperature for more than 2 hours.

When travelling, choose shelf-stable snacks such as dry cereals, crackers, raisins or prunes, fruit pieces, or vegetable sticks. Avoid meat or cheese sticks unless you carry them in an insulated cooler.

E. coli Foodborne Illness Outbreak: A Devastating Case Study

In early 1993, reports of a major outbreak of foodborne illness due to a rare strain of *E. coli* bacteria shocked the Nation. The outbreak was linked to undercooked hamburger patties purchased from a West Coast fast food chain.

Recognized as a pathogen in 1982, *E. coli* 0157:H7 has been associated with several foodborne illness outbreaks in recent years. A number of cases have been linked to undercooked ground beef and, to a lesser extent, impure water, unpasteurized milk, and low-acid apple cider.

Symptoms of *E. coli* foodborne illness include severe abdominal cramps, followed by watery diarrhea that often becomes bloody. Victims may also suffer vomiting and nausea, accompanied by low-grade fever. In some persons, particularly children and the elderly, the infection can lead to severe complications, including kidney failure.

While *E. coli* 0157:H7 can cause serious illness, it can be controlled by thorough cooking. Consumers should cook ground meat and poultry until the meat is no longer pink and juices run clear. When ordering hamburgers in a restaurant, ask that they be served medium or well-done.

In the wake of the outbreak, USDA has embarked on a number of new initiatives at the farm, meat plant, supermarket, and consumer levels to protect the public. For example, USDA is sponsoring research aimed at keeping food animals from harboring the 0157 bacteria in their systems, which includes efforts to develop a vaccine against the illness. USDA is working on improving detection methods to keep the bacteria out of meat plants, and instituting more stringent time and temperature controls in meat processing plants. It is also working closely with State and local public health agencies to increase effectiveness in avoiding and containing outbreaks.

Another important initiative is to require that all raw and partially-cooked meat and poultry products carry safe handling instructions on the package label. These instructions will guide consumers to steps they can take to ensure proper sanitation, cooling, and cooking when preparing meat and poultry products.

Preschoolers

This is an ideal time to teach food safety principles to your children.

Teach them to wash their hands after using the toilet and before and after handling foods.

Explain why some of their favorite foods—milk, juice, cheese, eggs, and hot dogs—need to be refrigerated.

Caution children not to eat cookie dough or cake batter that contains raw eggs.

School-Age Children and Teens

The independent school-age child can quickly prepare his or her own breakfast or after-school snack. Make sure that food safety is on the menu!

Tell children to wash hands before preparing or eating food. Always use clean spoons, forks, and plates.

Don't place books or book bags on eating counters or the kitchen table.

Throw away leftover sandwiches or other "refrigerator type" foods left from lunchtime.

Do not leave perishable items at room temperature. Remind children to return them to the refrigerator as soon as they are finished with them.

Caution children not to eat bread, cheese, or soft fruits or vegetables that look bad or have even small spots of mold.

Microwave Safety Tips for Older Children

If you give your child permission to use the microwave, start by holding a Saturday morning training session. Only children who can read should be allowed to use the microwave.

Parents should know that severe burns can and do occur from improper microwave use. Special packaging for kids' favorite foods like popcorn, pizza, and french fries can get too hot for kids to handle. Steam from popcorn bags can burn the eyes, face, arms, and hands. Jelly donuts, pastries, hotdogs, and other foods can reach scalding temperatures in seconds.

Food Safety Tips
from the Meat and
Poultry Hotline

1-800-535-4555

1. **Keep it safe, refrigerate.** Refrigerate foods you'll use quickly. Freeze raw meat or poultry you can't use in 1 or 2 days. Freezer should register 0°F; refrigerator, 40°F.

2. **Don't thaw food on the kitchen counter.** Bacteria multiply rapidly at room temperature.

3. **Wash hands before preparing food.** Wash hands and utensils after contact with raw meat and poultry. Wash cutting boards or other work surfaces too. Bacteria, often present on raw foods, can spread to other foods if you don't.

4. **Never leave perishable food out over 2 hours.** This includes marinating. No need to bring foods to room temperature before cooking.

5. **Thoroughly cook raw meat, poultry, and fish to at least 160°F internal temperature.** Juices should run clear and meat should not be pink. Do not partially cook food. Have a constant heat source, and never set the oven under 325°F.

6. **Promptly refrigerate or freeze leftovers.** Divide large quantities into smaller containers for quick cooling. Reheat leftovers to at least 165°F.

Food Safety for At-Risk Individuals

Foodborne illness is a much more serious concern for some people than others. Today a growing number of people are vulnerable to severe and chronic foodborne diseases due to compromised (weakened) health status.

Food risks for health-compromised individuals result from depressed or weakened body defense (immune) systems that do not protect against microbial invasions well enough. Some diseases or health conditions cause dysfunctions of the immune system, while immunity can be immature in infants and waning in the elderly. Without adequate immune system protection, extensive and life-threatening diseases can occur from bacteria and viruses on mishandled foods. As a result, these people must practice special precautions when buying, handling, preparing and storing food.

Persons With Weakened Immune Systems

Immunocompromising conditions can be caused by genetic disorders, chemotherapy, surgery, medications, and infectious diseases. For example, in persons with the HIV infection that leads to AIDS, certain cells called the T-helpers—which would normally stimulate the body's defenses and limit the invasion of unwanted microbes—have been destroyed. As a result, persons with AIDS are 20 to 30 times more likely to acquire salmonella infections, and 300 times more likely to be infected by Listeria monocytogenes. In addition, this leads to chronic diarrhea, malabsorption of nutrients, and undesirable weight loss.

Chronically Ill People

Chronic diseases also can damage organ systems involved in the body's defense and increase the risk of foodborne infections. For example, a person with a diseased liver, the body's primary filtering organ, is more susceptible to blood and other tissue infections. Other chronic and compromising diseases include diabetes, nonalcoholic cirrhosis of the liver, and cancer. Reduction of stomach acid associated with aging or surgical procedures has also been associated with foodborne disease.

Infants and Children

An immune system that hasn't finished developing, small body mass, and increased exposure mean greater risk and severity of foodborne disease for infants and children.

Infants have little natural immunity when born. In addition, premature babies may not even receive normal maternal protection through nursing, increasing their vulnerability to infection.

Older children are exposed to high rates of illness in schools and daycare facilities. There is less control of personal hygiene and more chance of spreading infections. Proven practices that limit the spread of foodborne illness in schools include monitoring handwashing by both staff and children and discouraging children from bringing home-cooked meals to school.

See page 189 on food safety for children.

The Elderly

The elderly make up an increasingly large portion of the population, with many persons suffering from chronic and immuno-compromising diseases. Studies show that as people age, their protective immune systems weaken. Medications and treatments, such as diuretics, antacids, and chemotherapy, can further limit resistance to foodborne infection. These high-risk factors can result in serious problems when the elderly eat foods with disease-causing bacteria or viruses. For example, Salmonellosis from improperly handled foods has caused severe illness and even death in elderly consumers.

Food Handling Recommendations for Persons at Risk

The rules for safe food handling given earlier in this chapter are especially important for at-risk individuals. Some deserve extra emphasis for those with special needs, and a few additional precautions are recommended for avoiding listeriosis.

- Never eat raw meat, poultry, or seafood, such as steak tartare or raw oysters or clams. In fact, meat, poultry, and fish should be well-cooked for persons at risk.

- Avoid foods with raw or undercooked eggs.

- Food should be served piping hot; if it's not, it should be sent back for further heating.

Avoiding Listeriosis

Pregnant women, the elderly, the very young, those with immune-compromising conditions, and those preparing foods for these individuals can decrease risk by:

Avoiding raw or unpasteurized milk.

Avoiding soft cheeses such as Mexican style, feta, Brie, Camembert, and blue cheese. There is no need to avoid refrigerated hard cheese, processed slices, cottage cheese, or yogurt.

Reheating leftover foods or ready-to-eat

The Interesting Case of Listeria Monocytogenes

Listeriosis is a rare but potentially fatal disease for those at risk. Persons over 60 years old and newborns have the highest incidence. The Listeria bacteria rarely causes illness in healthy people, but pregnant women are at risk for listeriosis, because of risk to the fetus. Listeria monocytogenes bacteria can grow—very slowly—at refrigerator temperatures on foods, and illnesses have been linked with ethnic soft cheeses, raw chicken, deli-prepared luncheon meats, and salads.

Symptoms vary and depend on the individual's susceptibility. Symptoms may be limited to fever, fatigue, nausea, vomiting, and diarrhea. More serious forms can result in brain infection and blood poisoning.

foods such as hot dogs thoroughly until steaming hot before eating.

Although the risk with deli foods is low, persons may choose to avoid these foods or thoroughly reheat cold cuts before eating.

Where to Go for Food Safety Information

The Meat and Poultry Hotline

USDA's Food Safety and Inspection Service operates a toll-free hotline to answer questions about food safety and nutrition. The Hot-line, staffed by home economists and registered dietitians, handled 100,000 calls in 1992. Callers can also hear food safety information by using the Hotline's Food Safety Information System, a series of recorded messages that can be accessed with touch-tone telephones. Over 50 food safety and nutrition messages are available 24 hours a day.

USDA offers and promotes food safety education. The Hotline staff works closely with the USDA Extension Service and other groups to advance this mission.

While many of today's consumers are extremely knowledgeable, people are routinely exposed to a tremendous amount of nutrition and food safety misinformation. By combining food safety advice with nutrition information, the Hotline has proved a boon for callers. The complexity of today's food marketplace and the ever-increasing number of new foods on the market has compelled more consumers to call the Hotline than ever before. A consumer calling about the safety of a meat or other product stored in his or her refrigerator can now find out how it fits into a balanced diet.

The Hotline can be reached at:
1-800-535-4555
In the local Washington, DC, area:
(202) 720-3333
FSIS Public Awareness Office:
(202) 690-0351

The Cooperative Extension System

Nutrition and food safety educational programs have been a cornerstone of the Cooperative Extension System (CES), a partnership of the Extension Service-USDA with State and county educators. The CES links the education and research resources and activities of the USDA, 74 Land-Grant Universities, and almost 3,150 county administrative units. The CES has an ongoing Food Safety and Quality national initiative which has resulted in a variety of program approaches to producing and maintaining a safe, wholesome food supply. You can also contact your local Cooperative Extension Service office for information and educational programs about the safe handling of food. Consult local government listings for the office nearest you.

Grill Our Experts With Your Food Safety Questions

Call the USDA Meat and Poultry Hotline for food safety facts

1-800-535-4555
Washington, DC 720-3333
10:00 am–4:00 pm Eastern Time

Professional home economists will answer your questions about proper handling of meat and poultry, how to tell if it is safe to eat, and how to better understand meat and poultry labels.

Appendix II
Where To Get
More Nutrition
Information

Sandra L. Facinoli
Coordinator, Food and
Nutrition Information Center,
National Agricultural Library

Do you want to know how much fat there is in your favorite ice cream? Is a family member doing a science project and are you helping with the research? Looking for a publication to hand out to your community youth or adult group? The USDA and the Land-Grant university system have professionals ready to help you find the answers and materials you need. Several electronic systems and networks are also available to assist you in finding food and human nutrition information.

USDA and Land-Grant Sources

Cooperative Extension Service

The Cooperative Extension Service has State, county, city, and area staff who link research-based nutrition, food safety, and food quality information with technology to help people improve their lives. These individuals are faculty and staff of Land-Grant universities located in each State across the country.

Telephone numbers and addresses for the more than 3,000 county and city offices across the Nation can be found in the government pages of local telephone books or by calling the local telephone information service. Ask to speak with the Extension home economist or nutritionist.

Food and Nutrition Information Center, National Agricultural Library

Nutritionists and registered dietitians help people find information or educational materials in the following areas of food and human nutrition: nutrition education, human nutri-

tion, food safety, food service management, nutrition software, and food technology. For example, the staff will help locate hard-to-find answers to questions, provide literature searches from the Library's bibliographic database, AGRICOLA (see explanation below), or assist you in finding the best audio-visual materials for a lesson or presentation. The center publishes Nutri-Topics and other resource lists on a variety of specific food and human nutrition topics.

The center has a food and nutrition software demonstration center, where an individual can preview any of over 200 software programs.

Contact:

Food and Nutrition Information Center
USDA/National Agricultural Library
Room 304
10301 Baltimore Blvd.
Beltsville, MD 20705-2351
301-504-5719 (automated system available 24 hours a day)
Fax: 301-504-6409
Internet address: fnic@nalusda.gov

USDA/FDA Food Labeling Education Information Center, National Agricultural Library

Located in the Food and Nutrition Information Center at the National Agricultural Library, this center is set up to assist educators, health professionals, and nutritionists locate information about educational programs related to food labeling.

Contact:

USDA/FDA Food Labeling Education
Information Center
Food and Nutrition Information Center,
Room 304
USDA/National Agricultural Library
10301 Baltimore Blvd.
Beltsville, MD 20705-2351
301-504-5719 (automated system available
24 hours a day)
Internet address: Gmcneal@nalusda.gov

**Meat and Poultry Hotline, Food Safety
and Inspection Service**

The hotline is staffed by home economists and
registered dietitians who can answer questions about food safety, storage, preparation,
and labeling (including nutrition labeling), as
well as nutrition questions concerning meat
and poultry products. The toll-free number is
1-800-535-4555; the hotline is staffed from
10:00 a.m. to 4:00 p.m., EST. In the Washington, DC, area call 202-720-3333.

Food and Nutrition Service

The Food and Nutrition Service administers
Federal food assistance programs, including
food stamps; food distribution; supplemental
food for women, infants, and children; school
lunch; school breakfast; special milk, child
care; summer feeding; and other child-nutri-
tion and family-food-assistance programs.
Information about these programs may be
obtained by contacting the following FNS
Regional Public Information Offices:

Northeast Regional Public Affairs Director
10 Causeway Street
Boston, MA 0222-1068
617-565-6418

Mid-Atlantic Regional Public Affairs
Director
Mercer Corporation Park
CN 02150
Trenton, NJ 08650
609-259-5091

Southeast Regional Public Affairs Director
Suite 112
77 Forsyth St., S.W.
Atlanta, GA 30303
404-730-2588

Midwest Regional Public Affairs Director
77 West Jackson St., 20th Floor
Chicago, IL 60602
312-353-1044

Mountain Plains Regional Public Affairs
Director
Room 903
1244 Speer Boulevard
Denver, CO 80204
303-844-0312

Southwest Regional Public Affairs Director
Room 5C30
1100 Commerce Street
Dallas, TX 75242
214-767-0256

Western Regional Public Affairs Director
Room 400
550 Kearny St.
San Francisco, CA 94108
415-705-1311

You may also contact:
Director of Public Information
Food and Nutrition Service
USDA
3101 Park Center Dr.
Room 819
Alexandria, VA 22302
703-305-2276

Human Nutrition Information Service

The Human Nutrition Information Service provides information for professionals and the general public on nutrition topics, such as the nutritive value of foods, food money management, dietary guidelines, guides for food selection and storage, and preparation of food. HNIS research includes the fields of food consumption, nutrition knowledge and attitudes, dietary survey methodology, food composition, and nutrition education. Requests for information and publications may be directed to:

Office of Governmental Affairs and Public Information
Human Nutrition Information Service/USDA
6505 Belcrest Rd., Room 344
Hyattsville, MD 20782
301-436-5196

Agricultural Research Service

ARS conducts research to ensure an adequate and safe food supply that meets the nutritional needs of American consumers. Promoting optimum health and well-being by improving the nutritive value of food is also a major objective of ARS. For information contact:

ARS Information Office
Room 450
6303 Ivy Lane
Greenbelt, MD 20770
301-344-2340

Electronic Access to Information

Human nutrition information is available through several computer-based systems. Electronic bulletin boards and databases are an important method of information exchange. They are accessible around the clock, so information is available whenever it is needed.

Internet

The National Research and Education Network (NREN), a part of Internet, is a worldwide network that can provide access to valuable information collections and services. Using Internet, you can search subject matter databases, participate in discussion groups, and send or receive electronic mail. There is a great deal of information available about using Internet. Ask a librarian, contact a computer specialist, or talk with friends, family members or colleagues who may already be using the network about where to get more of the details. Almanac, listservs, gopher, and wide area information server (WAIS) are some of the network information tools available. These networking tools allow you to explore and locate valuable resources anywhere in the world. All Land-Grant universities and many USDA agencies have computers connected to Internet.

The first step in getting access to Internet is to establish an account on a computer that is connected to the network. If you have questions about access, contact your local library or computer specialist.

Information servers called Almanac process information requests through electronic mail. Currently there are seven Almanac servers in operation. Their Internet addresses are as follows:

Location	Internet address
Oregon State University	almanac@ocs.orst.edu
Purdue University	almanac@ecn.purdue.edu
Extension Service-USDA	almanac@esusda.gov
North Carolina State University	almanac@ces.ncsu.edu
University of California	almanac@silo.ucdavis.edu
University of Wisconsin	almanac@wisplan.uwex.edu almanac@joe.uwex.edu (This is for the Journal of Extension)

To find out what information is available in Almanac, send an electronic mail (E-mail) message to one of the above addresses. In the body of the message type the command:

send catalog

Use lower case characters. Do not type any other text. For example, you can subscribe to *Food Market News* through the almanac site at Oregon State University

To obtain a users' guide, in the body of the message type the command:

send guide

It may take only a few seconds or several minutes for your request to be honored, and the materials will be available when you read the E-mail.

Gopher allows you to locate resources from hundreds of locations worldwide. This powerful tool permits you to access a library in another country as quickly as accessing the card catalog in your own State's library system.

The Cooperative Extension System currently operates seven gopher sites. You can access a site, for example, by using telenet with the address:

info.umd.edu.

This connects you with the University of Maryland's gopher. The menu path to reach the Extension Service-USDA gopher is "Other Gopher Information Servers"/"North America"/"USA"/"General"/Extension Service USDA Information. You can search for food, nutrition, or other related information.

Electronic Bulletin Boards
The Human Nutrition Information Service and the National Agricultural Library both maintain electronic bulletin boards that contain human nutrition information. To access an electronic bulletin board you need the following: a computer, a modem, a telephone line, and communications software.

Agricultural Library Forum (ALF). Produced by the National Agricultural Library, ALF contains a subboard called Food. The Food subboard provides access to information and publications from the Food and Nutrition Information Center, the FDA/USDA Food Labeling Education Information Center, and other Federal food and nutrition activities. Subjects covered include human nutrition, nutrition education, food safety, food service management, food technology, food labeling education, and food and nutrition software.

There is no registration fee for the bulletin board. You will become a registered user after you first log in. If you are unfamiliar with dialing into an electronic bulletin board system, you may get assistance by calling 301-504-5113.

Modem numbers: 301-504-6510, 301-504-5111, 301-504-5496, 301-504-5497.

Communications settings are: 8 data bits, one stop bit, no parity, full duplex. Terminal emulation should be none, ASCII, or TTY.

Internet Access: Telnet fedworld.doc.gov Register on this National Technical Information Service (NTIS) bulletin board system (bbs). Then select Gateway (D command), then select federal bbs (another D), then select 2 from the list for ALF. You will be automatically connected to ALF. When you exit ALF you will still be in the Fedworld system and will need to follow directions for exiting.

Nutrient Data Bank Bulletin Board. The Nutrient Data Bank Bulletin Board is sponsored by the Human Nutrition Information Service (HNIS) in Hyattsville, MD. It is operated as a public service to provide information about current HNIS publications and computer files on the nutrient composition of foods. There is no registration fee.

The telephone number is 301-436-5078 Internet access: telnet info.umd.edu

Communications settings are: 8 data bits, one stop bit, no parity, full duplex.

International Food and Nutrition Database (IFAN) (a computer-based information system)

IFAN is part of PENpages, a computer-based information system at Penn State's University Park campus. Penn State is one of the Land-Grant universities that are located in every State and that play key roles with USDA in conducting research and in providing education and information access for the public. IFAN is a full-text database containing documents including newsletters, fact sheets, research summaries, and other nutrition-related materials.

There is no registration fee for using IFAN. To access IFAN, you need a computer, modem, and communications software that is VT-100 or VT-102 compatible.

Modem number: 814-863-4820
Internet address:
psnutrition@psupen.psu.edu
After connecting, press <enter> until the prompt psupen> is displayed. Type <connect pen>. At the prompt, type the two-letter abbreviation for your State. Press <enter> to get to the PENpages menu.

For additional information, contact:
IFAN Editor
Penn State Nutrition Center
417 East Calder Way
University Park, PA 16801-5663
814-865-6323

Bibliographic Databases

AGRICOLA. AGRICOLA is a bibliographic database consisting of records for journal articles, monographs, theses, patents, software, audiovisual materials, and technical reports relating to all aspects of agriculture. The database contains information on human nutrition, nutrition education, food safety, food service management, food science, and food technology.

The database is available online through the commercial vendor, DIALOG Information Services. It is updated monthly. For information on subscription rates and fees, call 1-800-3-DIALOG. AGRICOLA is also on CD-ROM from SilverPlatter Information, Inc. For subscription rates for the disk, which is issued quarterly, call 1-800-343-0064.

The database is also available at university and college libraries, and at many public libraries. Ask a librarian or information specialist for assistance.

QUERRI (Questions on University Extension Regional Resource Information). QUERRI is a bibliographic database supported by the Cooperative Extension Services of Illinois, Indiana, Iowa, Kansas, Michigan, Minnesota, Missouri, Nebraska, North Dakota, Ohio, South Dakota, and Wisconsin. The food and nutrition materials listed in QUERRI are related to family and consumer issues. You will find the materials by conducting keyword searches in the database. Copies of the listed materials can be ordered from the distribution offices of the producing institutions.

There is no registration fee for using QUERRI. You will need a computer, modem, and communications software. You can connect either through a modem or Internet. When you connect to QUERRI the first time, select "How to Use QUERRI" from the main menu and go through a short tutorial.

Modem number:
515-294-(your baud speed)

Internet address:
telnet isn.rdns.iastate.edu

Modem settings: 8 data bits, one stop bit, no parity, full duplex.

Credits

Production Team, Office of Public Affairs

Deborah Takiff Smith Editor and Project Manager
Julie Olson Design Director
Ken Hammond Photography Coordinator
James Boykin Composition
Warren Bell Printing Coordinator

Working Group Contributors

Jacqueline Dupont and Ruth Coy Agricultural Research Service
Betsy Crosby Agricultural Marketing Service
Mel Mathias Cooperative State Research Service
Alden Manchester and Les Myers Economic Research Service
Bonny Wolf Food and Consumer Services
Devra Massey Food and Nutrition Service
Diane Odland Human Nutrition Information Service

Colophon

Printing
This book was printed on a Harris M-1000 web press in Kingsport, TN, on recycled 60-pound white offset book paper using vegetable-based ink. The cover is Kivar-9, cambric finish.

Design and Production
Text was created and submitted in WordPerfect. It was then formatted on an Apple Macintosh II using Microsoft Word 4.0, then imported into QuarkXPress 3.1 for page layout on a Macintosh Quadra 800. Figures were drawn by hand and scanned into Adobe Photoshop and finished in Aldus Freehand 3.1 and Adobe Illustrator 3.2. The cover design was created in QuarkXPress 3.1 on a Macintosh Quadra 800.

Typography
Body text is set in Century Old Style 10/13 x 16 Justified limiting hyphens to two and the hyphenation zone to one. Chapter heads, first degree subheads, and sidebar heads are Futura Bold. Sidebar text is Century Old Style. Author names and titles, tables, figures, and captions and photo credits are Futura Condensed.

Camera-Ready Art
All elements except photographs were submitted for film output on a 44 MB Syquest cartridge. Photographs were stripped in traditionally.